The west hill

Previously published works:
A Collector's Stories & Recipes, Opus Mundi, Ottawa / 1979
Time to Blow out the Lamp, Opus Mundi, Ottawa / 1980
One for sorrow, two for joy, Deneau Publishers, Ottawa / 1984

View from the west hill

MARY COOK

Mary Cook

Wallace Enterprises

Published in Canada by Wallace Enterprises
135 Judson Lane, Carleton Place, Ontario K7C 2S7

First Edition 1987

Cover photographs: Heather Lang-Runtz
Cover pictures of Krista Jane Kipp

Acknowledgements: The author would like to thank the following people: Val Nicholson, for her assistance; June Thompson, dressmaker; and Shirley Gobiel, who encouraged me to write the original stories for the CBC.

Author's note: Some of the people are real; some exist only in my imagination. And while some of the stories are based on actual events, others come from "mind-the-time" exchanges at family gatherings or from my mother's remembrances.

Canadian Cataloguing in Publication Data

Cook Mary, 1932-
View from the west hill

ISBN 0-9693026-0-6

1. Cook, Mary, 1932-
2. Farm Life - Ontario - Renfrew (County)
3. Renfrew (Ont.: County) - Biography
I. Title.

PS8555.0566V44 1987 971.3'8103'0924 C87-090171-0

PR9199.3.C66V44 1987

Printed and bound in Canada by
Love Printing Service Ltd., Ottawa, Ontario

No lovelier hills than thine have laid
My tired thoughts to rest:
No peace of lovelier valleys made
Like peace within my breast.

— Walter de la Mare
1873-1956

Contents

The west hill

The west hill. It was always a favourite spot of mine when we lived on a Renfrew County farm in the Ottawa Valley in the thirties. The hill, which sat like a large lump on the landscape, was uniquely formed in that a person could approach it from one side without having to climb a steep slope. It was called the west hill, of course, because it was west of our house. We could see it plainly by looking out our back kitchen window.

In the winter it was a wonderful slide hill where we took our home-made sleighs and an old, battered toboggan that Father managed to talk someone out of in exchange for a couple of bags of grain. When we went to the west hill to slide down it, we always circled it first in order to avoid the steep side. But, once poised at the top, we aimed our sleighs towards the Bonnechere River at the bottom and proceeded down the steep slope. Then, when the slide was over, we walked to the other side, and there we were at the top again. I was never able to figure this out as I thought at the time that a hill should be exactly the same on all sides.

The very top of the west hill was covered with tall pine trees and several sprawling maples. The maples stood out against the sky like big, protective soldiers, and it was under these trees our cows liked to rest on a hot summer's day. I often watched them from the kitchen window and saw that they, too, took advantage of the easy climb by going around to the other side to get to the top.

During a terrible electric storm one day we watched in horror as lightning hit a maple, killing most of our cows under it. It was a long time before I would go back to the west hill. I can still see Father and my brothers dragging those cows off the hill to bury them — and I remember so well the anguish and the worry that came from that accident. There was a concern that we would never recuperate from the loss.

But my fear of the west hill and the threat of bankruptcy subsided. Before the summer was gone I was back, sitting under the pine trees and eating the lunch I had brought in a little honey pail. I was a timid child back then, and the hill was the perfect place for me to be off on my own. Yet, I could still see our old log house, where I knew I could be in minutes if the need for escape arose in a hurry.

Sometimes my sister, Audrey, and I would go to the west hill to do our embroidery. I think I loved those times on the hill the best of all. We would pack all our coloured threads and the bleached flour bags we were working on into a sewing basket, and with a little lunch (I never liked to go anywhere without a little lunch) we would head for the hill. Audrey would have a quilt over her arm, and we'd spread it out under a tree. From the top of that hill we could see for miles. There would be Father and the brothers moving around in the barnyard below or Mother going to the clothes-line or the smoke house. Up there on the hill Audrey and I would talk about things that only two sisters could talk about. Even though I was much younger, those wonderful west hill talks always made me feel that I was equal to Audrey.

A patch or two of wild flowers grew on the west hill, and lots of buttercups. Audrey would pick a buttercup and hold it to my throat. If it cast a golden shadow, then I was going to marry a wonderful prince and ride off into the sunset and my life would be filled with joy and happiness forever. Wise as she was, Audrey always told me she could see a golden shadow.

Now, so many years after we left the farm, I still miss most the west hill and all it meant to us as children. When I returned to see it after being away for so many years, the hill looked exactly the same. And, as always, I still walked around to the other side to get to the top. So many things change but stay the same.

Everyday survival

It's difficult to recall those years of growing up on the farm in the thirties without marvelling at the ingenuity of the people whose everyday survival was an exercise in perseverance. Very little money changed hands among the farmers we knew because very little money was in circulation. Most people didn't even have bank accounts. It's hard to say if this was because there was no money to put into the bank or because of the abiding fear that the few dollars a farmer managed to deposit could be lost if the bank went out of business. Phrases like cash flow had yet to be coined. But words like barter, trade, and bargain were commonplace, with barter being the most common.

If there was any extra cash floating around, it was more likely to be squirreled away in the flour bin or under the corner of the braided rug in the parlour. Of course, everyone knew where the money would be stashed. How well I remember our parent's instructions that if there was ever a fire, grab the few dollars and run!

A very poor farmer was one who could not keep food on the table. This was because there was always plenty of meat, loads of vegetables in the garden, and fruit on the trees. The truth of the matter was our family ate well.

Over and above the everyday needs of our stomachs were other needs as well. School-books, boots, medicine, coal oil . . . staples not grown or produced on the farm had to be got somehow. To pay for these necessities almost every farmer we knew bartered.

As with most farmers, we raised chickens, turkeys, geese, beef, pork, and lamb. Amazingly, every scrap of every fowl and animal was used. Killed fowl was taken to the grocery stores in Renfrew, and in return for our staples our mother would negotiate with the merchant the amount of the bill. In those days, we were very lucky indeed if even the plumpest of chickens fetched seventy-five cents. But we counted on not only the meat of the fowl: the feathers would be carefully plucked and sorted as best we could into bags of down or coarser feathers. When we had a goodly amount, the bags were sold to a dealer for pillows and mattresses. As well, our mother took a long, hard look at every bird before it met its maker. If the chicken was still a laying hen she had a reprieve as we had several Renfrew customers who counted on fresh eggs from us every Saturday. We certainly couldn't afford to put an end to an easy few extra pennies. Good, large, brown eggs could bring up to fifteen cents a dozen — an amount that certainly wasn't to be sneezed at. Beef was commonplace at our dinner table. In addition, the hide was cleaned and dried, and it too was sold to the peddler who called at the farm regularly.

We often traded farm items with our neighbours. For instance, our old Model T Ford came to us when our father traded nine loads of gravel from our pit to a farmer who desperately needed it to build up his lane. It was simple: he needed the gravel and we needed the car. I have seen my father trade cows for a horse, a cutter for a wagon, and a few bags of oats for sheep.

And it wasn't above any of the people we knew in the farm community to bargain for a good deal either. Often we watched our mother spar with the grocery man for a better deal on her turkeys, or argue for more cash for the blocks of ice we drove to the creamery — ice that had been taken from the frozen Bonnechere River in the winter.

There were always a few things for which a farmer needed cold, hard cash. A store that sold drygoods or boots, for instance, had little need for a load of chickens. But if there was a good crop of potatoes, or the hens layed well that week, or several of the regular egg customers also wanted some fresh churned butter, there would be a bit of cash to buy a few yards of print or a badly needed pair of rubber boots. And if the returns were especially fine on a Saturday, we five children would each be given a few pennies to buy cent candy at Briscoe's store on the way home.

The thirties was a time when the phrase "hand to mouth" had real meaning. We grew, we cropped, we raised, we prepared for market, we bought the barest of necessities that the returns would allow. And then the whole survival process would start all over again. But, as youngsters, we children realized little of the financial hardships that surrounded us. Our bellies were full; we were ecstatic over a simple thing like a new, wooden pencil box; we laughed a lot (usually crying only if we felt physical pain); we believed with all our hearts that a higher being would take care of our every need. And we firmly believed that the gloomy stories of poverty and hardship, written in bold, black headlines in the *Ottawa Farm Journal*, were about another country far, far away from Renfrew County.

MY THREE BROTHERS, EARL, EMERSON, AND EVERETT, AND FATHER SPENT MANY HOURS CHOPPING WOOD AND FILLING THE SUMMER KITCHEN TO TIDE US OVER THE LONG WINTER.

Balls of string

Not too long ago a friend brought me a delightful, little magazine from Prince Edward County. In it was an article that, for me, turned the clock back almost forty-five years. The story was about string. As I read it, I realized that I, too, shared the same memories of that commodity and its importance to all who lived during the thirties.

Everything bought at the general store was tied with string — from the half-pound of black pepper in the small, brown paper bag, to the five pounds of sugar, also in a brown paper bag, to the loaves of store-bought bread. The storekeeper was certainly not stingy with the string as he sometimes wrapped it around a package several times. Cooked meat, which came wrapped in a lighter grade of brown paper that almost resembled tissue paper, was also tied securely with white string.

The string holder in the store sat under the counter. The string was taken to the ceiling and put through a closed end nail, from which it hung limply over the counter at the ready. Once the storekeeper had all the supplies gathered at one end of the long, oak counter top, he would pack them into a cardboard box, lifting the flaps to make the box higher and tying them securely with string. There was no such thing as a staple gun to do the job.

Once we arrived home with our groceries, the string was handled with the utmost respect. As the job of looking after it usually fell to the youngest in the household, it became my task to take the string off all the packages that were in the grocery box. It was very strong, I remember, but I was not allowed to cut the knots open with the scissors. So instead I used a large darning needle, or sometimes the tines of a fork, to poke away at the knot until it was freed.

Another of my jobs was to make sure the string was ready for its next function. Into a corner spot in a drawer of the wall cupboard I would put all the loose string. Here it would stay until, at my leisure, I had time to do with it what was always my chore. On the kitchen wall was a tin box, which was usually a replica of a little boy fishing, or a little fat pig, or some other caricature. This box held a ball of string, which I had rolled. I don't recall that anyone else in our family ever had to do the job: my older brothers and sister looked on the task with scorn, as if they were too old and mature to do something as menial as roll string.

When the ball was as fat as a hardball, I would take the string box down off the wall, put the ball into it, and feed the end out the little boy's fishing rod. It was up to me to make sure an end was sticking out at all times. Since the ball was made up of hundreds of pieces of all different lengths, and I was not allowed to knot it as the string then wouldn't go through the little fishing rod, I was constantly on the alert to make sure there was a new end hanging out, ready for use.

Any string left over from the ball was rolled into other fat balls. These could have tiny knots that were hardly visible, but the ends had to be cut off close to the knot. It was quite a laborious task to make the string ball appear to be one long, continuous piece. But this was necessary because the string from this roll was used for knitting dishcloths. Heaven forbid that the finished cloth would have masses of loose ends. These dishcloths were used by all the farmwives I knew in Renfrew County. After many wearings and washings they bleached out to a snowy white and were very absorbent. I had to make sure there were always a few balls of string ready for what my mother called idle fingers, which she wouldn't tolerate.

My old, maiden aunt, who spent the winters with us, had a unique use for string. She knit little caps from it, and these odd apparitions she wore to bed to keep a chill off her forehead, so she would say.

String played a very important role in our life on the farm.

Today, when I look around for a piece of string, I usually have a hard time finding one. Nothing comes tied with string anymore. Some country stores that are still trying to retain a general store atmosphere keep a roll on hand just in case a customer asks for some string. But most stores have switched to scotch tape in the name of progress.

When I think of all the uses we had for that simplest of commodities, and how it is slowly fading from use, I realize more than ever that, like the Model T, white porcelain hand-basins, huck towels, and home-made lye soap, string is fast becoming a cherished memory of life as it was lived in the thirties.

Garden of plenty

When time permitted, Father would help with the planting of the vegetable garden. But to a great extent the task fell on Mother's shoulders. It was a job she accepted as something that had to be done, and the sooner she got on with it, the sooner it would be out of the way.

Planting time, as I remember, was a time for aching backs and long foot baths in the washtub at night; it was also a time for mounds of muddy overalls and the smell of freshly turned earth.

When the land had sufficiently dried out after the spring rains, Father would hitch up the horse and make long, even furrows in the field that accommodated our garden behind the house. He was the best plower in the county, our mother said, and the straight lines of the furrows and the freshly turned rows of black loam attested to this fact.

Long since, Mother would have had her flats planted. Seeds would have come through the mail from the catalogue, and perhaps a few extra packets would have been picked up at Briscoe's store at Northcote or at Scott's Hardware in Renfrew. And by the time planting time had rolled round, the flats would already be sprouting six- or seven-inch high plants. Onions were planted from the brown bag, which came tied with string from the general store. They were usually the first vegetables planted from seeds to show their heads.

On the day of planting, Mother would put on a pair of old bib overalls, which she kept just for this purpose, and she'd tuck in one of Father's long-sleeved plaid shirts to keep off the mosquitoes. On her feet would be a pair of gumrubbers tied securely with binder twine. I can remember looking at her and comparing her appearance with what she wore every day. I was always dismayed at the contrast. At any other time she wore crisply starched, cotton house-dresses with sparkly clean, white pinny aprons over them and laced, black shoes on her feet.

Dressed as she was for planting, she looked in my mind for

all the world like one of the scarecrows we put up in the garden to fend off intruders.

Mother especially liked to plant immediately after a good rain. She insisted the earth was more responsive to the young seedlings. However, if there was a long, dry spell and it appeared that to wait any longer for the planting would be disasterous, Mother would have one of my older brothers hitch up a horse to the stone boat. These weren't actually boats but rather two logs held together by boards. The boys would then load on two or three small barrels, take the stone boat down to the Bonnechere River, and fill the barrels with river water. As she planted, Mother would pail out water along the rows to soak the earth. By the time this chore was finished, she was soaked to the skin and the mud from the garden would be caked to the overalls like plaster.

Our vegetable garden was huge out of necessity. Not only were the sand bins in the cellar filled with enough to see us through the winter, but Mother canned and pickled hundreds of jars as well. Also, she hauled a goodly portion of the garden vegetables to Renfrew over the summer where our fresh vegetables were sold door-to-door. They commanded a healthy price: five cents for a big bunch of green onions, twenty-five cents for a large bag of new potatoes, and as much as fifteen cents for a basket of ripe tomatoes. So it was essential that our vegetable garden produce a good yield.

Mother had theories about what would grow best and why, and when we children were called on to help, we were given a mind-boggling set of instructions. Onions were to be planted a finger deep, potatoes two shoes apart, the cucumber seeds staggered, and the top of the bean hill watered. We found the job back-breaking and dirty, but Mother would accept no excuses. She considered the chore built character, and I can attest that we had enough character-building to last us a lifetime.

The planting went on for many days. Even a soft rain didn't delay the job. In fact, Mother would praise the Lord when she got up in the morning and discovered that gentle drops of rain were falling from the Renfrew County skies. Those were the mornings we didn't stop to red the kitchen but hurried into our garden clothes and tore out to the field. We worked fast and furious to get as much planted as possible so the seedlings would take full advantage of the gentle moisture.

And when we came in from the garden, we would be ordered to strip down to our skin in the woodshed. Heaven forbid if any of the mud was brought onto the clean kitchen floor. Then one after the other, we would climb into the big laundry tub that had been filled with warm water from the reservoir, and we'd be rubbed down with a piece of yellow home-made soap until our skins burned.

Many was the time we would stand by the garden fence and wait for the first signs of life to peep through the soil. When we saw the first growth, we'd rush to the house and tell our mother that the carrots were through or that the lettuce had just made its appearance. To us, it was a miracle. To plant a tiny seed, to watch it burst through the soil, and to have it end up on someone's dinner table twelve miles away in Renfrew or in our root cellar.

Many things made those Depression years easier to bear — like close communities and knowing that everyone around was in the same circumstance. That big family garden reassured us we would have full bellies even when the Renfrew County fields were covered with snow.

ALTHOUGH FATHER WAS BEST AT GROWING FLOWERS, MOTHER TENDED THE PEONIES, WHICH SHE ESPECIALLY LOVED, HERSELF.

The labour of spring planting

We could always depend on having our Saturdays planned for us in the early spring every year. There was no skipping off early in the day for a game of ball at the back of the school yard or a run in the bush with our old collie. Once my father, by his secret German methods, determined there would be no more frost in the night air, Saturdays in May were completely taken up with the serious business of planting. And every one of us was expected to help.

Our vegetable garden, like every other farm garden we knew of in Renfrew County, was huge by today's standards. Early in the season, Father would hitch up King to the plow, and long, straight rows of black loam would unfold like pages in a book. I always marvelled at how, without ever raising his eyes to look ahead, Father could end a row that was as straight as a die.

After the plowing, he would hitch the horse to the harrow, which to me always looked like a giant version of the rack our mother used to toast our bread over the coals in the Findlay Oval in the morning. This apparatus would rattle over the furrows and smooth out the lumps of loam. By the time Father had criss-crossed the garden from corner to corner and end to end, the earth would be as smooth as a blanket.

The actual planting of the garden was one chore we five children hated. It was hard labour, which kept us either bent over like a jack-knife or with our knees in the dirt for an entire day. I especially remember the ordeal of planting potatoes and onions — both were staples back in those Depression years. It seems to me now that we planted enough to feed most of Renfrew County. But potatoes and onions were cheap and grew quickly. And, as my mother always said, the potatoes were filling and the onions kept away the colds in the winter.

Once Father had the garden soil flat and smooth and just to his liking, we created an assembly-line system. This by no means eliminated the work but at least allowed the job to be completed as quickly and efficiently as possible. When Father had dug little hills in rows with the wide blade hoe, we emptied the bags of potatoes into the wheel barrow. Straining under the weight of the burden, my older brother pushed the load from the house to the very end of the garden. My sister, sitting on the ground, cut the potatoes into sections with the butcher knife, being careful that each one was left with an eye. One or two of us would then put the cut potatoes into granite pails and walk the rows, dropping the pieces into the hills. All the time Father would be checking to see that not too many and yet not too few cuttings were used. My job was to follow those who were planting and, with a hoe that had a short handle to compensate for my size, I would cover the potato hill with the earth. Still another brother would follow behind me with a pail of well water and dowse the spot I had covered.

We found the planting of onions a more distasteful job, however. Each of us took a row and, with a good supply in five different granite basins, we would get down on our hands and knees, plunge our fingers deep into the ground to make a home for the onion and then sink it in. We had to be careful not to cover the hole too soundly else the onion would not be able to breathe, as Father had warned us. All the time he would be walking the rows like a general inspecting his troops, and he would tap us gently on our backsides with the hoe as he passed: "Your row is off centre, Mary" or "You don't have to drown them, Earl." And so it went for the whole day.

When the planting was over and our bodies were caked from our chins to our toes with Renfrew County loam, we would run to the Bonnechere River, which snaked through our farm. Like convicts released from a long jail sentence, we would strip to our flour-bag underwear — unaware of any inhibitions — and, with a great running leap, we would fly into the swimming hole.

It was then that a marvellous transformation would come over us. As energy-sapped children, we were barely able to drag ourselves down the last row to plant the last onion. But we were reborn under the magic spell of the Bonnechere River. The laborious task of planting the vegetable garden was over and done with for another year.

The hand-me-down box

I used to think that Aunt Lizzie, my father's sister, had the seasons backwards. Twice a year she sent — out of a sense of duty, I am sure — a huge, aluminum-lined tea box filled with hand-me-down clothes that her two sons, my uncle Jack, and she could not, or would not, wear any longer. Every summer we got a huge box full of winter clothes; every winter, just before or immediately after Christmas when the snow was blowing across our field, a box of summer clothes arrived.

As Aunt Lizzie had no daughters, there was rarely anything in the box for me, although occasionally a small box of embroidered hankies would be tucked inside. Once I remember she sent me a hard, rubber ball with red, white, and blue stripes on it. (Aunt Lizzie was very patriotic.) Sometimes there would be a dress or two that would fit my sister, Audrey. But, because Aunt Lizzie dressed in the height of fashion, Mother refused to let Audrey wear them to the Northcote school. Most of the items in the big, aluminum-lined tea box were men's suits and pants, breeks for my brothers, and tweed caps. We figured the men in Aunt Lizzie's family had to be the best dressed in Regina because it seemed, back then, that every time a box came it held an overcoat.

There were only so many suits and overcoats my father and three brothers could wear on the farm. Their best clothes were reserved for Sunday church, and what we called their next-to-best were kept for going into Renfrew on a Saturday night. At the Northcote school all the boys wore bib overalls and plaid shirts except my brothers, who always dressed as if they had some place important to go when school was out. This was because my mother felt bib overalls and plaid shirts belonged in the barn, a notion which, Father insisted, she brought with her to the farm when she moved from New York City. My brothers were the best-dressed boys at the school, but no one dared razz them because they were also the biggest.

As there were always plenty of white dress shirts in the hand-me-down box, my brothers wore a white shirt and tie to school every day. And always breeks, those full-legged trousers that ended at the knees. Now, most of the time Aunt Lizzie sent suits, but Mother simply chopped the pant legs off at the knees, put a tight cuff on with a button — and there were the breeks.

I don't recall the box containing anything as fancy as a sports coat, but there were lots of suit coats. However, the boys preferred the cheap windbreakers we could buy at Briscoe's general store. These hung from a high wire at the ceiling, and Mrs. Briscoe had to climb a little ladder to get them down when one was sold. Emerson always got to wear the new windbreaker because he was the biggest. When he outgrew it, Everett inherited it. Finally, when there wasn't much left but the buttons, Earl, the smallest of the three boys, ended up wearing the windbreaker until it was beyond repair. I doubt that Earl ever had a new windbreaker all the time we lived on the farm.

Audrey and I didn't fare so well. It seemed to us that our brothers were always much better dressed than we were. And we lamented loud and long about the injustice of it all. So Mother tried to make amends by taking apart the overcoats that came regularly and fashioning skirts or jumpers for us. At first we were excited about the whole idea. We saw Mother rip the seams open, press each piece out flat with a damp cloth and, using an old skirt as a pattern, cut out new garments for us. Mother was not a particularly good sewer, but she did her best with what she had. The material in the overcoats was very heavy, so the first time I wore one of the skirts made from heavy overcoat melton cloth I could hardly sit down. The skirt stuck straight out in front of me, showing my navy blue, fleece-lined bloomers.

So then Mother started taking apart the suit coats, but there was scarcely enough material for a jumper or skirt. We often ended up with the front one colour while the back was another. And Audrey and I were expected to be grateful and overjoyed by these new additions to our scant wardrobes.

We did sometimes get blouses made from white shirts, however. These we loved because they had long sleeves and, even though the buttons were on the wrong side, we covered those nicely by wearing bows at our necks and letting the ends hang to our waists.

Even though the hand-me-down boxes rarely contained anything that Audrey and I could put on our backs and wear, we were thrilled when it came time to go to the CPR station in Renfrew and pick it up. It was years later after I began running my own house when I fully realized that it was the spring and fall closet cleanouts that had us get winter clothes in summer and summer in the winter. But, whenever they came, they were a much welcomed and appreciated supplement to what was, for us, an otherwise meagre wardrobe.

ALTHOUGH COUSINS RONNY AND TERRY WORE BOUGHT CLOTHES FROM THE MOST PRESTIGIOUS STORES IN MONTREAL, MINE WERE INVARIABLY HAND-ME-DOWNS, LIKE THE LITTLE BOY'S SUIT I'M WEARING, WHICH CAME IN A BOX FROM AUNT LIZZIE IN REGINA.

Red hair and blushes

As a young child I was especially prone to sudden bursts of blushes. My mother said they were a direct result of my fiery red hair and claimed that all redheads were so afflicted. However, my brother Emerson, whose hair was identical in colour to mine, was spared from this terrible adversity. Once again, I came to realize there were some injustices in this world that were beyond my comprehension.

I would blush either for absolutely no reason or when my teacher, Miss Crosby, cast a beady eye in my direction after posing some vague question for which I had no answer. Instead of trying to remember even a shred of detail, my concentration was spent attempting to keep my face from turning beet red. Of course, this never worked and I would feel myself breaking out in a cold sweat. I was convinced that absolutely everyone in the Northcote school was well aware of my change in colour.

My older sister, Audrey, ever the healer of wounds, tried to assure me there was absolutely no change in the shade of my face. But before I ever reached full glow, Emerson was bound to put his hand to his mouth and snicker into his palm, which only brought on a worse bout of embarrassment.

Emerson once told me that if I blushed too hard my hair would bleed because the blood would have to go someplace. This made perfect sense to me at the time and gave me something else to worry about.

I developed all sorts of little tricks to help me over these blushing spells. Not many met with much success. I sometimes tried to bury my entire head inside my desk drawer when I felt a flush coming on. At other times, I found that if I pressed a cold notebook to my face while in the middle of a blushing spasm, the spell went away. It was best if I was outside because I could simply run to another part of the schoolyard. But inside the schoolroom I was trapped and had to deal as best I could with what I considered a very serious malady.

Marguerite, who did everything in her power to cause me anguish while I was a pupil at the Northcote school, never blushed. She used to add to my misery by pointing out to everyone within earshot that "Mary was going into her act again." This caused my cheeks to burn even more.

Now, so many years later, I realize the things that should have embarrassed me gave me not a moment's concern, whereas those incidents that I should have been able to pass off without a murmur sent me into spasms of anguish. For instance, singing on a corner in Renfrew with the Salvation Army band when we were devout Lutherans had no affect on me at all. I felt perfectly at ease. However, if the librarian asked me a simple question, such as did I enjoy the books, I would turn beet red and run for cover.

I discussed the malady at great lengths with Audrey, who assured me that I thought it was much worse than it actually was. In complete defiance of Mother, who said the two were related, Audrey also told me that blushing had absolutely nothing to do with my red hair. Her advice to me was, when I felt a spell coming on, I was to think of something very funny — like pretending to see the person to whom I was speaking standing in long underwear. I confess this didn't work.

But the best bit of advice Audrey gave me was to go quickly to a mirror and take a good look, and then be assured that most of my affliction was inside my head and not on my face. Of course, by the time I found a mirror, the spell invariably had passed and what I saw was a perfectly normal face with perfectly normal colouring, slightly ruddy from a generous spattering of freckles. This exercise helped me more than anything to overcome what stands out in my memory as a devastating event in my life.

I also began to notice that other young people in the Northcote school were prone to blushing. Even Miss Crosby turned a bit red when the school inspector walked in unannounced.

These observations did much to help me come to terms with the fact that I would probably go on blushing until I was grown up and away from the Northcote school. It was years before I got over the affliction, in fact. But I came to accept it as another cross I had to bear, like red hair, skinny legs, flour-bag underwear, and a hateful brother. All these I blamed on the Depression.

Velvet

I could never understand, nor could I accept, the idea of horse trading all the time I lived on the farm during the thirties. Especially when, in most cases, you took one or two horses for the trade and brought one or two back with you. But horse trading went on all the time.

In those days little thought was given to show horses, or what your team looked like hitched to a wagon. People were more interested in the horse's ability to do the work.

I was especially fond of the horses. Ideally, I would have preferred to keep them all until they silently faded away. But, of course, this was not the way things happened. My favourite horse was called Velvet. She, too, came in a horse trade. She had a white star on her forehead and four white feet. In the winter her coat was thick and warm. Velvet was small, much smaller than the other horses. This, I suppose, is one of the reasons why I loved her. But, unfortunately, this was also the reason she was slated for the horse trade.

Father called her a luxury horse. And there was no room on the farm during the Depression for a luxury horse. When he traded a big work horse for her, it was because he was sure she would grow into a large mare, produce other large horses, and pull her load with the best of them. Poor Velvet, however, was destined to be small.

I could stand beside her and wrap my arms around her neck, which pleased her greatly. In fact, standing in the yard or the barn, waiting to be petted, was one of Velvet's favourite pastimes.

When it became apparent that Velvet wasn't going to grow any more, Father announced he had to think of getting rid of her in a trade. My heart sank to my boots: I begged him to let her stay, and tried to reason with him that Velvet would be just perfect for the buggy and the cutter and that it really didn't matter much if she didn't grow any more. Father said, with what I thought was a high degree of callousness, there was no room for horses that couldn't earn their keep, and that any one of the work horses could pull either the buggy or the cutter as well as work the farm.

I couldn't imagine why Father didn't get rid of King, who frightened the starch out of all of us. Granny Hines said the horse was evil. He was known to trample chickens in the barnyard, kick down a gate that stood in his way to freedom, and chase other horses away from the feed and watering troughs. Once when King was tied in his stall, I had taken a good, long look at his eyes, which Father always said were a dead give-away to a horse's temperament. He warned that one should be careful if there was any white of the eye showing because it meant the horse had a mean streak in it a mile wide. Well, King sure had lots of eye-white showing. Whenever I dared to go near his stall — which only happened when I knew he was well tied — like a raging dog he would bare his teeth and his ears would flatten out against his head. I knew he would just as soon bite me as look at me.

It did no good trying to convince Father that King was the horse to trade. He said King was the best work horse on the farm, and it didn't matter much how ugly the horse was as he didn't keep them around for their looks.

I knew I had lost the argument when one Saturday morning I looked out the kitchen window and saw Velvet and two other horses tied behind the big sleigh. Father was on his way to Douglas to trade. I had no appetite for the apple fritters, my favourite Saturday morning breakfast, but put on my heavy winter clothes and went outside to say my 'goodbyes' to Velvet. She was many hands smaller than the two other horses that were tied to the wagon. Oblivious to what was in store for her, Velvet was eating hay off the back. Father had used the curry comb on her, and her coat looked shiny and thick in the early morning sun. I couldn't bear to hug her, and the tears froze to my cheeks as the sleigh made its way out of the barnyard. I watched it round the corner at the gravel pit, with the three horses tied together on a rope behind, and wondered what kind of farmstead they would be going to.

Father was gone most of the day. The traders met at a farm near Douglas that wasn't more than eight miles away. Mother, too, was wondering what was keeping him. But then, just as my brothers were going out to start the evening chores, we saw way down the lane the team coming with three horses tied behind. It looked as if Father had made an even trade: in place of three brown ones, he was bringing home two grays and one brown. I wasn't much interested but stayed at the kitchen window with my head between the geranium plants as Father came through the gate near the house. And then my heart started to race because between the two greys was Velvet. Home again. I grabbed my coat off the hook and, without stopping for galoshes, tore out the door.

Father, seeing how thrilled I was, stopped the sleigh so that I could plant a hug around Velvet's drooping neck. "Wasn't going to trade down" was all he said. I followed the sleigh to the barn, unhitched the little horse and, without asking Father, gave her a dipper of oats. At supper, Father said the only horse left at the trade was one not any bigger than Velvet — and it had a sway back. He also said he had a real good look at its eyes, and there was too much white showing for his liking. One evil horse on a farm was enough as far as he was concerned. Velvet was home to stay.

ALTHOUGH I CONSIDERED VELVET AS MY HORSE, EMERSON OFTEN TOOK HER OUT OF THE BARN. THIS WORRIED ME, AS IT WASN'T ABOVE HIM TO ANTAGONIZE HER.

Oh, for that store-bought jam!

Nowadays a thick slice of home-made bread slathered with freshly churned butter and topped with home-made strawberry jam would be considered a rare treat. In fact, anything turned out in one's own kitchen is supposed to quicken the pulse and cause mouths to water. But back in the thirties, when I was growing up on a Renfrew County farm, we thought that anything bought from Briscoe's General Store held more allure than anything Mother could turn out on the Findlay Oval.

This did not discourage her, of course, from baking about twenty-four loaves of crusty bread a week, churning up a batch of butter every Saturday, and preserving everything that looked like a berry, come fall.

I remember what a treat it was for us if, on those rare occasions, Mother found a few pennies that would buy a loaf of store-bought bread or a few slices of thick bologna for our school lunches. But the rarest treat of all was the big pail of strawberry jam that, through a means of juggling the Saturday supplies money, Mother was able to bring home once a year from Briscoe's store.

Father thought this was the most extravagant act he had ever witnessed. Can you imagine buying jam when the shelves in the cellar were full of jars and sealers filled with everything from gooseberry marmalade to crab-apple jelly! But Mother knew how much we loved the store jam. For some reason, when we took sandwiches made of jam from that store-bought pail to the Northcote school, we felt just a cut above those who had to content themselves with home-made preserves. We never failed to point out to everyone within earshot that this was store-bought jam right from Briscoe's. It was important to emphasize where the jam came from as this added credence to the statement that it was bought.

The jam came in a sealed, shiny pail or can. There was no snap-on lid like today's containers have. The pail had a label wrapped all the way around it — and I can remember so well the picture of a little girl in a berry patch, picking big, juicy, red strawberries and putting them into a pail, just like the one our store jam had come in. Over the picture was the name Betty's Jam. I loved the label: when Mother put the pail on the table at breakfast, I would turn the label towards me so that I could gaze at the young girl picking the big, luscious berries. They weren't anything like the tiny strawberries we picked every summer along the railway tracks that ran through our farm.

Once, Emerson, a brother, picked off the label, and I was hysterical. I thought at the time this was the cruelest gesture he had ever taken against me.

The pail held about four cups, so we were expected to use the jam sparingly. Also, once it was gone, we had to resort to the home-made preserves in the cellar. So I took it as a personal duty to make sure the privilege was never abused. And I had no qualms about screeching to Mother that Emerson or Everett had taken two spoonsful instead of one.

We could make the tin of Betty's Jam last a good month. We weren't allowed to have a jam sandwich just any old time of the day. The jam was reserved for breakfast and school lunches only. After all, the four-cup tins sold for seventy-five cents — a portly sum — and sometimes, in order to pay for it, Mother would talk old Mr. Briscoe into three or four pounds of home-made butter as a trade. But, because she knew how much we loved the store-bought jam, I believe she would have bought it for us at any price.

There was only one way to get into the can of Betty's Jam, and that was with one of those ancient can openers. You slammed the point into the top of the container with the heel of your hand and then, using the opener in a sawing motion, chewed the can until you had an opening that you could bend back. Of course, you couldn't put the lid back on, so after breakfast Mother, who was meticulously clean and fussy, would fold down the tin flap and put a clean piece of cheesecloth over the top, tying it with a piece of string.

When the tin was empty, we five children vied for the final treat. Mother would have us draw straws. With a hand closed tightly around the pail to keep from tearing oneself on the jagged opening, the winner took a crust of bread and captured every last drop of that precious jam from the bottom of the tin.

A cloud of pale green organza

The call had come in from the station-master in Renfrew, just as it always did when the hand-me-down box arrived from Regina. Aunt Lizzie packed and sent the box to us about twice a year. It was always filled to the brim with clothes that her two sons had outgrown. Rarely was there anything in it especially for girls, but Mother was clever at embroidering flowers on a boy's coat sweater or turning a jacket into a garment suitable for Audrey or me.

Nothing in that box was ever wasted. If something fit you, you wore it.

One year — I remember it especially because Easter had come early — there was still an abundance of snow on the ground and the air was damp and cold. The station-master had called to say the box had arrived, so Father had hitched up the sleigh and, with all of us as passengers, drove on the side of the road all the way into Renfrew. We were all excited: the box could have contained an array of brand-new clothes right out of the Eaton's catalogue.

The box looked the same as always — like a big, wooden cube, lined in tin or foil, with the lid hinged with wire. Mother said it originally held bulk tea, so we had no idea where Aunt Lizzie managed to find two of them every year.

It took the three brothers and Father to lift the box onto the back of the sleigh. All the way back to Northcote the boys draped themselves around it, as if it might tumble into the ditch at any moment and their precious cargo would be lost. Audrey and I sat on the quilt-covered bale of hay at the front. But we kept a watchful eye on the box, hoping with all our hearts that, just once, it would contain something that didn't look as if it had come off our male cousins' backs.

As soon as the box had been propelled into the kitchen, Everett ran for the crowbar to pry off the lid. The rest of us stood around in anticipation while Mother barked out instructions that there was to be no grabbing. If the unpacking was not done in an orderly fashion, she warned, the box would be pushed into the summer kitchen where it would remain until after Easter.

The box was opened, and there under the first layer of Regina newspapers were the usual items — boy's caps, sweaters, and breeks. Emerson laid claim to a pair of fairly new rubber boots as they fit him like a glove. In fact, that was how the clothes were divided. As each item was unpacked, it was tried on: those who got a fit got a new item to add to their scanty wardrobe.

As usual, there was little for Audrey and me. Audrey claimed a red toque, and I had about given up hope by the time the shiny bottom of the box could be seen. But then Mother reached down and brought out a parcel wrapped in white tissue paper. The note on it said 'For Mary'.

The fact that I was Aunt Lizzie's favourite niece did little to endear her to my brothers and sister. Yet, this was the first time ever that I had received a parcel marked especially for me in the hand-me-down box.

I untied the string with great care. Inside was a cloud of pale green organza. I lifted up what was, for me then, the most beautiful, little dress I had ever seen. The dress was covered in lace and bows and had small buttons at the neck. Aunt Lizzie had also enclosed a pair of short, pale green sox and matching hair ribbons. I held the dress up to me: it was a perfect length. Only fleetingly did I think of how the short, green sox would look teamed with my heavy, brown, laced brogues. I was far too excited about the dress.

Never before had I ever had a store-bought fancy dress. My brother Emerson said it would be months before I could wear it because of the weather. But I begged Mother to let me wear the outfit to church on Easter Sunday. So when the day broke as snowy and cold as any other winter day, my heart sank. Thankfully, Mother knew how much it meant to me to wear the dress: I was allowed to wear it, but only if I was wrapped in a heavy blanket and carried both to the sleigh and into church as she wouldn't dream of having me expose my bare legs in the cold weather. I agreed to everything. I would have even worn Father's old muskrat coat, which hung in the drive-shed, if I had to.

Not surprisingly, once I put on the dress and sox, I began to shiver from the cold. The goose-flesh stood out on my legs and arms like hives. I was forced to stand beside the Findlay Oval to soak up as much heat as possible. Just before we were ready to leave for church, I put on my winter coat and Mother encased me in a heavy patchwork quilt. I was carried to the sleigh, and then into church. Inside, despite the cold, I took off my coat and folded it in the pew beside me. When Emerson made fun of my bare legs, I became aware that the short, green sox had been noticed by everyone at the front of the church.

Yet, this Easter Sunday was one of the most glorious I had ever spent. I thanked God for blessing me with an aunt like Aunt Lizzie. And, even when the fire had died down in the stove at the back of the church and the goose-flesh was causing my skin to turn blue — even then, I was the happiest that I remember being for a very long time.

EARL HOLDING A BARN CAT, EMERSON WITH UNCLE LOU'S WIRE-HAIRED TERRIER, AND ME.

The prettiest vegetable garden

Before the snow was off the ground and the first groundhog had shown its head, Mother would anticipate the arrival of the seed catalogues. They would come with a splash of colour across the covers, and just looking at them would stir up thoughts of hot summer days, flower beds, fresh vegetables, and the sweet smell of mustard pickles stewing on the back of the stove.

Mother loved those seed catalogues, and she would pour over them for hours. Using a sheet of foolscap, she would make a list of the seeds she was ordering, then revise that list until only those items she could afford were on it. The vegetables would be ordered first. If there was anything left in the budget, she would write down an order for pansies and asters, her favourite flowers.

Once Mother had adjusted her order to include what she would like and what she could afford, it was put in the envelope and sent off with the mailman. During the thirties, the orders were processed with astonishing speed. It seems to me, now, the little box of seeds came back in a matter of days.

I remember one particular year when the Montreal cousins had been with us over the winter for the first time. The youngest of the cousins, little Terry, was so angelic we hardly ever heard a peep out of him. But his brother, Ronny, was another kettle of fish. He was constantly in trouble and, as Father often said, would tax the patience of the Pope. Terry loved the bright colours of the seed catalogues. Although he would spend hours going through the Eaton's catalogue, it always took a back seat when the Steele-Briggs book arrived.

Mother was so pleased to see young Terry take such an interest in something other than watching his brother get into trouble that she allowed him the privilege of fetching the parcel from the mailbox and opening it on the kitchen table. Terry was doubly thrilled when Mother said he could be in charge of all the little packets. He spent hours going over them, arranging them in colours, and trying to separate the flower envelopes from the vegetables.

When the seeds arrived, Mother's main concern was with getting her planting boxes ready. Upon clearing a little patch of snow down to the ground, Father would dig up some earth and bring it into the house to thaw out behind the Findlay Oval. Then Mother would poke away at this earth until it was as soft as newly sifted flour. She would mix in any left-over green tea and its leaves, which she insisted had a great deal to do with the healthy plants she produced each year. Next, the earth would be spread out in little, flat, wooden boxes saved from year to year for just this purpose. The entire process would take several days because the earth had to be just right.

Terry, in the meantime, never let the seed packets out of his sight. Even when it was time for bed, he would take the box upstairs, putting it on the braided rug near his head just in case anyone had designs on taking over his job.

Finally, the day arrived when Mother was to plant the little boxes. It was a Saturday, so we were all home from school. The boxes, when spread out on the kitchen table, covered the entire top. And while Mother and the rest of us went to the barn to finish the chores, Terry was left with the boxes and the seeds. He was told to stir up the earth so it would be well broken up when he and Mother did the planting. We had never seen him so excited. As we headed for the barns, he was last seen sitting at the table with the seed packets clutched to his chest as if he feared someone was going to snatch them away.

When we came back, Terry was sitting in the rocker with the empty seed box and the wooden spoon, which was covered with earth. Beside him on the floor was a mixing bowl, and in it were the contents of every seed packet from the box. Black beans, carrots, dahlias, pansies — they were as one.

Terry looked as proud as punch that he had everything ready for the planting. Mother's look of dismay was short-lived. One had only to see Terry's enormous black eyes of innocence to realize no malice had been intended. Had Ronny done the deed, however, the repercussions would have been heard as far away as Admaston.

This is why, that year, we had the prettiest vegetable garden in the county. Here and there, between the carrots and the turnips, grew little clusters of asters and pansies.

Turnips fit only for pigs

No one knew more about the importance of gardening than the person who struggled to survive during the thirties. Full bellies depended largely on full root cellars, and the ample tables our relatives raved about on their Sunday visits to the farm would not have been possible without the acres of vegetables we harvested each year.

The seed catalogues came to the house early in the new year, and Briscoe's store in Northcote displayed box after box of small envelopes of seeds — all priced at five and ten cents a packet. Early in the year my mother would plant small, oblong, wood boxes with seeds (I remember thinking it was a miracle when the small sprouts would poke through the earth). The boxes were lined up on the window sills, on the small kitchen table, and on anything else where the plants could benefit from the sun's rays.

Mother had a marvellous time with her plants. Knitting needles pushed in the earth with little scraps of paper stuck on to the ends would identify what was expected to show itself in due time. Always there were cucumbers, and radishes, and tomatoes. But one vegetable, which Mother refused to plant because she considered it fit only for feeding the pigs, was never planted. And that was the turnip. Mother once told Father that in New York the turnips was scorned like the smallpox. Even when Aunt Lizzie called the turnip by its fancy name 'rutabaga', it did absolutely nothing to enhance the vegetable in Mother's eyes. She steadfastly refused to make it a part of her spring planting routine.

Father did everything in his power to convince her that she was missing a rare treat. He even suggested that, if she just once tried his favourite German recipe, he was sure she would change her mind. But Mother wouldn't bend. Turnips were meant for pigs — and that's all there was to it. Thus, the row on row of turnips we planted each year, even though they were kept in the root cellar with the rest of the vegetables, never found their way to our table.

Then one Sunday my mother badly twisted a knee climbing out of the buggy after church. Father, in a rare show of concern, ordered her to bed and announced he and the children would look after the chores and see to supper. Mother put up no resistance and hobbled to the downstairs bedroom with the *Philadelphia Enquirer* in one hand and the big, red, rubber hot-water bottle in the other.

I am positive that Father's concern was in a large part brought about because he saw an opportunity to try out his talked about, but never tested, German turnip recipe. I also believe that, had Mother known what he was plotting in the kitchen, she would have miraculously recovered.

Supper rolled around. Father put on another block of wood and revved up the old Findlay Oval. Soon a pot of water was rolling to a full boil. Into this pot a large turnip that had been chopped was dumped; in another pot several big apples that had been brought up from the root cellar in the skirt of Mother's white baking apron were added. I thought of sneaking into the bedroom to tell Mother that Father was cooking turnips, but I was so fascinated at the sight of him in the kitchen getting supper that I didn't want to do anything that might put a stop to this performance.

When the turnips and the apples were done to his liking, Father drained them and dumped the two pots together in Mother's large baking bowl. Then he beat them like a man possessed until they were smooth and golden. He scooped out a towering spoon of fresh butter and plopped that in too. To this he added a teacup full of brown sugar and gave the mixture another stir for good measure. During this procedure all of us stood around the stove. I was thoroughly convinced that even the addition of things I loved, like apples and brown sugar, would do nothing to mask the flavour, which Mother had convinced us would turn a dog's appetite.

Father insisted on serving the supper plates himself. Alongside the thick slices of salt pork, which he had fried crisp and golden, he put mounds of the turnip mixture and a heaping spoonful of pan potatoes, which had been cooked in bacon drippings. "By Gar, there's nothing like good, old, German stick-to-your-ribs kind of food," he said with relish as he filled the last plate.

One taste was enough to convince us that we had been missing a great German delicacy for years. And when Mother hobbled out to the table and tried the turnips on the very end of a small teaspoon — as if they were medicinal — she, too, reluctantly agreed the turnips certainly didn't taste anything like she had expected.

The German turnips became Mother's specialty. Call it pride or what you will, but I never heard her admit that Father had introduced her to the turnip. And the only taste the pigs got thereafter of ***that*** vegetable was when some had been left over in the root cellar after the next season's crop was harvested.

PORK WAS VITAL TO OUR SURVIVAL IN THE NINETEEN-THIRTIES. LARGE BARRELS FILLED WITH SALT PORK SAT IN THE CORNER OF THE KITCHEN, AND HAMS HUNG IN THE SMOKE HOUSE. THESE AUGMENTED OUR FOOD SUPPLY DURING THE LONG WINTERS.

In the heat of the summer

I remember the Renfrew County summers of the thirties as being hot and sticky. The sand outside our back door would cake in the burning sun, and the ground would crack in the barnyard from lack of moisture. The farm animals would be listless and wander from the watering trough in the middle of the yard to the shade of the old maple trees behind the barn to find some relief from the relentless heat of the days.

But inside our log house, square and solid, the rooms were cool and inviting. The Findlay Oval would long since have been moved to the summer kitchen. The braided mats, which covered the pine floors, would have been rolled in copies of the *Renfrew Mercury* and tucked under the beds to stay there until the first signs of fall touched the Renfrew County air.

When temperatures soared — the days were far hotter, it seems, than they are now — the old house was a comfortable haven.

The secret, it seemed, was to keep the house dark. We had no windows in the doors — they were just great slabs of pine unadorned with glass or trimmings. During the hot summer days, we were ordered to go in and out of the house with a haste that had us slamming the doors with such gusto that the house rattled on its foundations. "Once you let even a bit of heat inside, you'll live with it until September" were Mother's words of wisdom.

There were no blinds on the windows, only scant, flour-bag curtains, starched crisp and clean and hanging like two narrow pieces of paper. The curtains offered little protection from the hot, cruel sun. But each morning, before the sun had a chance to penetrate the little, square panes, Mother climbed on a chair and hooked quilts over the curtain rods to black out the light. Blankets covered every window, upstairs and down, and I can remember that we groped our way around the pitch-black interior of the house like a sightless visitor, feeling for chairs and doorways.

When the sun went down and there was no risk of even a glimmer of light coming in through the windows, the ritual of taking down the quilts began all over again. And, when darkness crept into the Renfrew County sky, the windows were thrown open and the night air was allowed to waft through the old log house, cooling the interior.

If we had company during the day — say on a Sunday afternoon — they were taken into the dark parlour where just a corner of the quilt was lifted and secured to the window frame. But the moment the visitors left, the quilt was hastily let down again.

Meals were eaten in the grape arbour if weather permitted. The summer kitchen would be throbbing under the heat of the raging Findlay Oval and to eat in the main house would mean losing the cool air. So, with the exception of breakfasts, meals were carried outside: with the hanging vines forming a canopy over our heads, we ate all our meals on a long table retrieved each year from the drive-shed and covered with oil-cloth.

One of us stood guard over the table, swishing flour-bag tea towels over the food to make sure not one fly came in contact with what we were putting in our mouths. Next to the heat Mother hated flies. I was always amazed at how she could spot from the summer kitchen a fly circling the table in the grape arbour. Then she would holler, "Keep those towels going out there. I see a fly over the bread plate."

At night, when it was time for bed, we would go upstairs to the bedrooms. As they had been kept in total darkness all day, they were as cool and inviting as a spring rain. The feather tickings would be covered with home-made sheets. When the quilts were taken off the windows, the cool night air coming in from the Bonnechere would fill the room. Invariably, towards morning, we would feel the need to reach to the foot of the bed and pull up the light, summer, patchwork quilt that was kept there for just such a purpose.

Today, electric fans and air conditioners artificially keep our homes comfortable in the summer. But it seems to me now, as I recall those early days, that our old log house was more like a place of refuge on those hot and humid summer days. Outside, it could be hot and sticky and our clothes would cling to our bodies. But inside it would be cool and inviting — a haven from the heat of the summer.

Not born for a New York Stage

The best stroke of luck since the Depression hit — a golden opportunity — was how Mother viewed it. I thought it was a calamity, the most awful development to occur in my young life.

It all happened because one of Mother's butter and egg customers taught dancing in Renfrew. This lady took a particular liking to me: when I delivered the produce and stood at the door waiting for the money, she would tug at my ringlets and tweak my cheek as if I were an infant. As Mother always gave thirteen eggs as a dozen and her pounds of butter well exceeded sixteen ounces, this particular customer decided she would do something nice in turn.

It was a lovely Saturday that found Mother and I driving up to the dance teacher's big, yellow, frame house in Renfrew. She was expecting us and was out on the big veranda, which circled the house. Mother waited in the buggy while I handed over the shoebox of brown eggs and home-made butter. I was to ask for fifty cents. But before I could do so the young woman had bounded off the veranda. She confronted my mother with a bizarre plan: if Mother would continue to supply butter and eggs, I could have free ballet lessons.

Needless to say, Mother was overjoyed. She still had the smells of Broadway and the Radio City Music Hall in her nostrils, and she thought the whole idea was perfectly splendid. I shifted from one foot to the other and wondered when — and if I dared — to offer an objection. I grew up in a time when children did exactly what they were told. But, in this case, if I had to take ballet lessons, it would be only after protesting greatly.

The teacher suggested that Mother simply change the delivery time so that I could be dropped off early. While Mother got rid of the rest of the produce, I would spend the time being taught dancing with a class of young Renfrew girls.

The whole idea sounded absolutely terrifying to me. First of all, I had no desire to dance ballet. Furthermore, I was terribly shy, and the very thought of performing with complete strangers sent chills up my back.

But I knew I had lost the battle. Mother was too caught up in the idea of having a daughter who, as she put it, could eventually end up on a New York stage. No, it was an opportunity that simply couldn't be missed.

The following Saturday I got out of bed with a heavy heart and made one final attempt at trying to convince my mother that dancing the Highland Fling at the Saturday night dances in Northcote was one thing, but ballet dancing was an entirely different story. Nothing worked. Mother was happier than I had seen her in months. She sang while she washed the eggs and packed them in shoeboxes and while she wrapped the freshly churned butter into bricks. She couldn't wait to get on the road. She buttered two slices of home-made bread and put jelly between them for me to take as a lunch. The sandwich was put into a paper bag, along with a clean pair of short, white sox that I wasn't to put on until I had entered the dance teacher's living room.

When we reached the house Mother abandoned me at the door. I was ushered into a parlour with shiny, wood floors and where all the furniture had been pushed back against the wall for the class. One girl was busy cranking the Victrola. About seven or eight others, all dressed in short, organza skirts and long, white stockings, were kicking their legs in the air while holding on to pressed-back chairs. I looked down at my wool jumper and brown brogues and wondered how I could escape. I was told to take off my skirt and my shoes. That left me standing in flour-bag underwear and brown-ribbed stockings. I quickly put on the white sox. The girls were whispering behind their hands, and I knew they were talking about me.

The teacher worked with me for a while but finally had to spend time with the advanced pupils. After what seemed an eternity, we were told to break for lunch. I was the only one who had sandwiches in a brown paper bag. I ate alone in a corner of the room, feeling more miserable than I had ever felt in my life. The afternoon was no better than the morning, and I knew I would never get the hang of it. The next Saturday I begged to stay home, but Mother again emphasized what a marvellous opportunity it was for me to have free dance lessons.

Eventually the Saturday sessions became an accepted part of my life. But I always felt apart from the Renfrew girls, and I was never accepted as one of them.

I would like to say that I became adept as a dancer, but alas I didn't. I felt much more at home, in my old, brown brogues, step dancing to Alec Thom's old fiddle at the Saturday night dances. And any dreams my mother had of me becoming a star on a New York stage ended when the dance teacher moved to another town. My lessons had ended, happily for me, as abruptly as they had begun.

THE BUGGY WAS LOADED WITH PRODUCE BEFORE MOTHER AND I TOOK THE TWELVE-MILE RIDE INTO RENFREW, WHERE SHE DELIVERED VEGETABLES, CREAM, AND BUTTER AND WHERE I MADE A VALIANT ATTEMPT AT LEARNING TO DANCE UNDER THE TUTELAGE OF A PROFESSIONAL TEACHER.

What is a heart?

"You're breaking my heart" — usually said with a touch of sarcasm in the voice, somewhat in the same vein as "give me a break" — is a common phrase used nowadays. But back in the thirties when I was still young enough to take every statement literally, any reference to the heart conjured up visions of a huge, foreign organ beating away in my bony chest, an organ that was very fragile and vulnerable to the most subtle suggestion. And I perceived the hearts of others to be the same.

This image I had of the human heart can be traced back to an expression I overheard my mother use one day. A neighbour who lived closer to Douglas had passed away a few months after her husband had died in a farm accident. When the news came to our house through the network of the party line, I heard Mother say to someone on the other end, "Poor soul. She died of a broken heart."

Now this gave me great cause for concern. As was usual when I had something important to weigh over in my mind, I escaped to the hayloft over the barn where I could analyze the comment and come to some — albeit misguided — conclusions.

I barely knew the old soul who had died, but I was able to conjure up her face to memory quickly, a talent I had developed early in life in relation to anything terrible or dreadful. As farm-wives went in those days, the woman was not very big. I immediately pictured her brown, muslin dress pulled tightly across a scant bosom, the last outfit I had seen her in at the Lutheran church several Sundays previously.

I knew exactly what a heart looked like: sharply pointed at the bottom end with two, large half moons at the top that met in a cleft — just like the hearts I had seen many times on my valentines. Due to an over-active mind, I was able to picture the old woman's heart lying in pieces close to her navel, which is where I had assumed it had slipped when it had broken. I imagined it had left a great, gaping hole under her rib cage. My diary tells me that I went to bed that night, convinced that any sadness that came into my life could render me with the same condition. Right then and there, I made up my mind that I would do everything in my power to keep my heart from breaking into a million pieces over some calamity. I had no idea how I was going to accomplish this feat, but I was determined to try.

When my parents once talked about another wealthy neighbour who let a relative go off to the poor house rather than give her a home, they said he had no heart. You can imagine how this statement distressed me. I had no idea how this man could have functioned without that piece of his body beating away inside. I assumed that someone had taken an x-ray, just like they did when I got my first pair of shoes in Renfrew, and determined that where his heart should have been was a great, yawning hole with not so much as a vein inside.

Another neighbour was accused of having a heart made of stone. As it happened, this neighbour was a big hulk of a man who had a large, curving back and hunched shoulders. It was natural, therefore, for me to picture that inside his chest he harboured a large stone instead of a heart. And that the weight of it, such a burden as it was, pulled the top part of his body forward into a stooped position. I found it difficult, however, to visualize how a heart that was made of stone could beat, but I assumed God had created some miraculous system, which I never once questioned.

I suppose all this misguided comprehension could have been cleared up simply enough if I had gone to Mother and voiced my concerns. I thought about doing this several times, but then another phrase dealing with the heart would come to mind and I would reconsider.

Once Mother had said she was frightened so badly that her heart had sunk to her boots. I don't have to tell you that I immediately pictured it travelling through her veins, past her kneecaps, through her ankles, and into her brown, laced brogues. How her heart got back up into her chest I had no idea. But the statement gave me enough concern that I wouldn't dare risk a repeat performance.

Escape from the farm chores

There wasn't a boy of the thirties whose heart didn't beat a little faster when he was told that the farm chores could be forgotten for a few days and that he could take himself and his fishing gear to the river. My brothers looked forward to those few precious hours on a summer afternoon. Once the word came from Father, they wasted little time in collecting everything they needed.

Most of the fishing gear would have been ready for just such a break — the rods standing in the drive shed, rolls of cord, an old tin pail with a fresh supply of dew worms — and a couple of sisters would be ready with a lunch in a brown paper bag. And, just maybe, they might be allowed to hold the rod for a few minutes, but they had no desire to disentangle a fish from the hook on the line. Such a distasteful chore was left to the boys.

More for something to do than as an act of readiness, the boys always had a pail of worms sitting in the ice-house. At night, when the dew was thick on the grass, they would go out with the lantern and pull the worms from the ground. They would put them into a pail already filled with a mixture of grass and damp soil. My sister, Audrey, and I loathed picking worms and would have nothing to do with the job. Instead, we watched from the upstairs bedroom window as the brothers, stooped over like gremlins from another land, moved about the grass in the shadow of the lantern. When they had what they thought was a goodly number, they would put a round piece of tin over the pail, cut out from an old stove-pipe for just that purpose. A heavy stone would be placed on the tin on orders from Mother, who would have put an end to the boys using the ice-house in this way had she ever found one of the worms crawling around in the sawdust. She found them just as distasteful as my sister and I.

The fishing rods were nothing more than the straightest branches that could be found. The branches would have been stripped of their humps and bumps with a jack-knife and the ends smoothed down with sandpaper to provide a good grip. The other end would have a small groove cut out of it, into which was tied the stoutest piece of string the boys could find. And on the end of the line a large safety pin with its jaws open or a horse-blanket clip filed down to a sharp point would be attached. No elaborate fishing rods and reels for the boys of the thirties.

I can remember the day a favourite uncle brought a bamboo rod with a great spring to it. For some reason, it never caught on; the boys still preferred their favourite branch, honed down to their liking.

When they had everything ready, the boys would take off their shirts, change into their oldest bib overalls, and roll the legs up to their knees. With bare feet, a straw hat to shade them from the sun, and their rods over their shoulders, they would head for the Bonnechere.

The old raft the boys had built to explore the river would be tied to a tree trunk on the shore. They would let out the rope as far as it would go so that the raft hovered in the middle of the river, and they would make a great chore out of getting all the equipment in just the right spot for easy access. The pail of worms sat in the centre of the raft, while the three boys sat with their backs to each other and dangled their bare legs and feet into the water. Father once told them they should keep their feet perfectly still, or else they would scare away the fish. But then the boys never planned on catching much anyway.

Audrey and I would position ourselves under the biggest oak tree we could find. Spread out on an old quilt on the grass and moss, our lunch beside us, we read our favourite books, played snap, and dressed and undressed our dolls a hundred times. We had to talk in whispers because the brothers insisted any noise would send the fish scurrying to another part of the river. As for the boys, they sat motionless with their backs straight as dies, barely moving except to toss the weighted string in to the Bonnechere for another cast.

Occasionally, but only occasionally, they would catch something besides the countless sunfish, which seemed to be the only form of life living in the river. Sometimes they would hook onto a mud pout, which Audrey and I thought were the ugliest creatures we had ever seen. When this happened, they would roar at the top of their lungs, and the hideous fish with the long sprouts coming out of the head would be tossed into a pail of water to be lugged home.

The boys cleaned the fish on an old stump behind the barn. Mother insisted that the mess attracted flies, so the job had to be done well away from the house. The boys were the only ones to eat the fish, which Mother dutifully cooked in a butter-filled iron frying-pan. Having watched the fish being caught, cleaned, and dried, any desire my sister and I had for fish was instantly killed. Mother said the fish always tasted of weeds, and Father insisted that sunfish and mudpout were never meant for the table.

Catching the fish was just an added bonus to the outing. The greatest thrills came from getting ready, the quiet time on the river — and being excused from the regular farm chores.

THE BONNECHERE RIVER WAS A FAVOURITE FISHING SPOT FOR MY BROTHERS, ALTHOUGH IT OFFERED LITTLE IN THE WAY OF SUSTENANCE FOR OUR TABLE.

To market, to market . . .

Mother never missed an opportunity to make an extra dollar. When her garden came up luscious and full — as it did most years when the weather co-operated — she was able to take into Renfrew baskets of produce, which she would barter for our weekly supplies. But Mother also saw that her rich garden could travel farther afield and bring even more returns, with a bit of extra work and time.

She knew Ottawa well, having been raised there. She had played on the streets where the Skyline Hotel now stands and had slid down Nanny Goat Hill. The Ottawa Byward Market was also a familiar place to my mother as Aunt Vanetta used to take her as a little girl on Saturdays to help lug home the bags of fresh vegetables and fruit.

This is why, many years later when she was a farmer's wife living in Renfrew County, Mother saw in the Byward Market a chance for our family to make a few dollars from the abundant garden that filled the better part of a field at the back of our old log house. She saw no reason why we couldn't load up the old Model T and head to the market in Ottawa to try our hand at being produce farmers. Father was dead-set against the idea, but Mother freed him from the task by announcing she intended to do it on her own with one of the children to help. Besides, she really couldn't afford to give up precious space in the car for him when the seat could be put to better use.

One Saturday morning, long before the sun was up, Mother and I crept down into the cellar with the coal-oil lamp to retrieve the baskets of fresh vegetables that had been picked just at sundown the night before. As Mother had lifted out the back seat of the car and parked close to the outside door to the cellar, it took us only minutes to arrange the produce. When we were finished, the car looked like a small garden plot. She left just the bare edge of the front seat for me to sit on. Boxes of vegetables on the floor forced me to keep my feet suspended. I had to keep them this way, Mother said, so that they wouldn't make contact with the produce — I had grave doubts I would be able to hold out until we arrived in Ottawa.

When Mother turned the car around in the front yard, it was still pitch dark, and I secretly wondered why we had even bothered going to bed the night before. We roared out the lane — Mother and me and the vegetables, with a lunch packed in a brown paper bag that I held on my lap all the way.

The sun was just starting to come up — it seemed to me we had been hours on the road — when we reached the city. By the time we reached the market, wagons and vendors had long since established themselves along the street. It was then she found out the best spots had already been taken. But Mother was not the least bit daunted. She simply manipulated the old Ford until it was up against the back of the wagons. Then she opened wide the four doors, stationed me at one side and herself on the other, put on a spanking white, flour-bag apron, and was ready for business.

When I reflect back on that day, I wonder why a policeman didn't move us on. But, apart from a few annoyed looks from the other vendors, no one objected to our being there. Business at the start wasn't as brisk as Mother would have liked it — of course, we weren't in the best spot. But she rectified this by taking armsful of vegetables and walking up and down the street hawking her wares. I was almost overcome with joy when I made my first sale, and thrust the few cents deep into my sweater pocket for fear someone would come along and take my money.

It seems to me we were cleaned out long before noon. The pocket on Mother's apron was bulging with coins and a few dollar bills. She allowed me to climb in the seatless back of the car and sort the coins into piles of dimes, nickles, and quarters. It seemed like an awful lot of money to me at the time.

We ate our lunch at the side of the road going home, with our backs against a tree — and with our money in an empty basket in the back of the car. It was a glorious feeling: I thought we were rich beyond words.

This was the first of many trips to the market in Ottawa. Even though we always sold everything we took in and came home with handfuls of coins and small bills, Father never thought the returns were worth the effort. Once he tried to figure out how much profit we actually had when the price of gas, the wear and tear on the old car, and a full day away from the farm were calculated. But he never could convince Mother that she hadn't discovered an easy road to new-found wealth.

The tattle that never was

Tattling was just not tolerated by Mother. She couldn't bear for us to tell tales on each other. On those rare occasions when we rushed to her with stories of a brother's or sister's indiscretion she would raise a hand high in the air and say, "Stop, I don't want to hear it. I don't like telling tales out of school." To her, tattling was akin to lying or stealing.

I can remember one time in particular when tattling would have given me such marvellous satisfaction. Marguerite, my worst school enemy, was glad — like the rest of us that year — when the school year ended. We had emptied our desks, scrubbed the entire room, washed the windows, cleaned the ashes from the pot-bellied stove, and wiped the chalk-boards. We were sitting in our seats and chatting to Miss Crosby, as we always did during the final hour. This was the only time pupils were allowed to talk aloud, and we all took advantage of the rare treat.

Miss Crosby was asking each of us what we were going to do for the summer. None of us had anything wildly exciting to relate. I said I might, just might, be going to Arnprior on the train to stay overnight with my Aunt Nellie and Uncle Henry. Not to be outdone, Marguerite said she was going to the Ottawa Exhibition. I didn't believe her: imagine going all the way into Ottawa for the exhibition when the Renfrew fair was close by and handy. The Ottawa Exhibition indeed. But leave it to Marguerite to top everyone's story!

Miss Crosby's eyes travelled to the old clock at the back of the room. It was time to close up the school. She walked to the door at the back, running her hand over the window sills as she went, and straightened a box of chalk on the long table that ran against the back wall. The little, flat boxes of chalk had been filled with all the pieces from the blackboard ledges, and would await our return in September. After one final look around, she was satisfied that everything was in order. Miss Crosby then went to the doorway and readied herself to shake hands with each of us as we filed out, our books under our arms.

Marguerite was right in front of me. As we passed the chalk table, her hand shot out. She captured a box and tucked it between her books. I was stunned — and Marguerite knew I had seen her. She not only wore a smug look, but her nose was in the air a mile. I well remembered the time I had taken four pieces of coloured chalk when I was a first-grader, and that my mother had made me walk the three-and-a-half miles back to the Northcote school with the chalk. But a whole box! And, moreover, Marguerite was old enough to know she was stealing. After all we were at Fourth book.

Well, I thought to myself, I'd soon fix her. Finally I would have my revenge against Marguerite for all those hateful things she had committed throughout the year: for always having store-bought bread in her lunch; for wearing white stockings and black patent shoes to school; for boasting about never having to wear hand-me-down clothes; and for buying her underwear out of the Eaton's catalogue.

I couldn't wait to get to Miss Crosby. After what seemed a century, Marguerite was shaking the teacher's hand and doing that silly curtsy she always did when she wanted to impress people.

I was next. Here was my chance. I was squirming in anticipation, and the palms of my hands were sticky and wet. I knew my face was beet red because I could feel it burning. Then Miss Crosby was pumping my arm. "Have a good summer, Mary." She saw me hop from one foot to the other. "Is anything wrong?" I looked ahead at Marguerite, who had turned ashen. She knew what I was going to do, and her face wore a look of absolute terror.

"Is anything wrong Mary?" Miss Crosby repeated. "I just wanted to tell you, Miss Crosby," I started. I took a final look at Marguerite, who looked as if she was going to die right there. "I just wanted to tell you, Miss Crosby, that I am going to learn to drive the tractor this summer. Father said I am old enough."

Like a wash of cool rain, relief flooded over Marguerite's face. She waited for me outside, but the last thing I wanted from her was her thanks. "I saw you take that chalk, Marguerite," I hissed between gritting teeth. At this she turned on her heel and raced back to the door. "Miss Crosby, I must have picked up this box of chalk with my school bag. I'll just set it back on the table." Miss Crosby beamed at her prize pupil and patted her bouncing, artificially curled hair.

I remember — especially on that particular day — feeling absolute hatred for Marguerite, who couldn't do anything wrong and whose main purpose in life (or so it seemed) was to make my life miserable. And I remember feeling then that sometimes there wasn't any justice.

THE NORTHCOTE SCHOOL WAS A VERY MODERN BUILDING FOR ITS TIME. EVEN THOSE OF US WHO WERE ITS STUDENTS DURING THE NINETEEN-THIRTIES THOUGHT IT WAS JUST A CUT ABOVE SOME OF THE OTHER ONE-ROOM SCHOOL HOUSES IN THE VALLEY.

The scooter surprise

That we would ever own a scooter was beyond our wildest dreams. Scooters were the rage in the thirties. Each time we went into Renfrew with our parents, we saw the town kids running their scooters on the sidewalks, and we envied them as only farm children living through the Depression could.

The scooters ran strictly on leg power. Two small wheels joined onto a flat platform, and a small set of handlebars were used for steering. You balanced with one foot on the platform and used the other to push the scooter along the ground. The faster you put your pushing foot to the pavement, the faster you travelled.

On these excursions into Renfrew, we would stand beside the buggy and watch the town kids scooter by, their faces crimson from the effort. We longed to try one out but wouldn't dare ask — and no one ever offered.

Then one day Father arrived at the farm with a scooter. We had no idea how he came by it — probably in one of his bartering deals — but we never bothered to ask, we were that excited. The scooter was a little the worse for wear with its paint scratched and the foot platform dented, but to us it looked perfect. The day Father brought it home just happened to be when our cousin Ronny from Montreal was on one of his extended holidays. He immediately informed us he was well acquainted with scooters, adding that he had at least seven at his house in Quebec. We didn't believe Ronny for a minute, but we didn't argue, we were so happy with our new scooter.

All of us wanted to try it at once. But it was finally decided that we would draw straws for the first go. I never liked this system because, it seemed to me anyway, whoever held the straws always ended up being first. That's exactly what happened this day too. Emerson, who was holding the straws, won.

He settled a chunky leg on the foot platform after pointing the scooter up the driveway that circled the pump. But as soon as he put his weight on it, it sunk about four inches into the sand. And no amount of pushing would budge it. We certainly didn't anticipate this turn of events. Ronny, who said he was too heavy for the scooter, wrestled the thing from Emerson. Unfortunately, he was also well rounded. Like Emerson, he met the same fate. Even when the scooter was moved over on the grass, the results were not much better. The scooter moved, but not with the same results that were achieved when the town kids got it revved up on the cement pavement.

As we knew he would, Ronny suddenly had a brain wave. We'd just take a plank, lean it against the back of the high wagon, and run the scooter off that. It took the seven of us to haul a big plank, which was resting against the side of the barn, over to the wagon. The plank was more than a foot wide and about three inches thick. It certainly looked as if it would give us a good run downhill on the scooter.

We climbed up on the wagon and stood in line, waiting for what we knew was going to be the thrill of a lifetime. Since it was Ronny's idea, he reasoned he should be the first to go. Ronny got poised with one foot on the platform while the brothers steadied the scooter on the end of the plank. "Let 'er go," Ronny yelled. The plank was only about twelve feet long, and Ronny careened down it like a high wind.

Then the little wheels hit the dirt and the scooter ground to a halt. Instantly, Ronny flew over the handlebars like a high diver and landed about eight feet away with the scooter upside down, its wheels spinning. His face was full of sand and his knees were scraped. The brothers at first couldn't decide whether to laugh or run, but when they saw he wasn't killed they decided to laugh. This further infuriated our Montreal cousin. Ronny kicked the scooter, sending it another few feet in the air, and decided this was as good a time as any to repeat all the things he didn't like about our Renfrew County farm.

After this disaster we didn't think we would be able to use the scooter we had all craved. Obviously, it wasn't going to go far without cement pavement. And the closest pavement was twelve miles away in Renfrew. And that's how it happened that every Saturday we loaded the scooter into the back of the wagon, or into whatever vehicle was chosen to make the trip into town for the week's supplies. While our parents shopped and bartered, we took turns scooting up and down the streets with our hair blowing and our faces flushed from the effort. And we felt not quite so deprived and more like the privileged kids from Renfrew.

The magic of the mail

One person above all others served as a link between our community and the rest of the world during the thirties. He was the one who kept us abreast of news of our relatives who lived many miles away and who caused our blood to surge through our veins in anticipation as we awaited our seasonal order from the Eaton's catalogue.

This person was the rural mailman. As I remember him from my days on the farm in Renfrew County, he was constantly attentive to the job at hand. During the heaviest snow storm, the hottest weather, the thickest fog, we could count on him to always bring the mail. I remember his buggy well. As far as buggies go, it was dilapitated and had a black painted canvas top, which folded down when the weather was fair and offered scant protection in a downpour. At the mailman's feet was a large, canvas bag with a draw-string top, and inside were the bundles of mail yet to be delivered. And on the seat beside him, all in perfect order, were the letters and parcels destined for our road. He seemed as contented as the old nag that pulled the buggy — never much in a hurry — but was as punctual as the CPR freight train that passed through our property on its daily run to Pembroke.

The mailman was built not unlike my father. A slight man, he always wore an old, straw hat and the inevitable pipe hung loosely in his mouth. As he farmed down the Northcote road we knew him also as a neighbour.

On our days at home we watched for the mailman, just as if he was a visiting member of royalty. We would hear the clop-clop of the horse's hooves first, and by the time he reached our old, tin mailbox several of us would be lined up in the lane to take the mail. If he came while we were at school, our mother would discreetly wait until he had passed and then would walk to the end of the lane — but not before she looked to see if the box was turned parallel to the road. This meant there was something inside. A lid facing the road was a sign that there was no mail for us that day.

In those days it was pretty exciting to get a letter, and I can remember how we marvelled that an aunt in Chicago or a friend in Montreal had mailed a letter to us and that it had found its way to Renfrew County. We children thought this was one of the most marvellous feats of the times. Sometimes if our Eaton's order was too bulky to go inside the mailbox, the old mailman would throw the reins over the gate and walk up the lane with the parcel. The excursion would give him the excuse to stop over for a bite to eat and a cup of green tea. "Just to tide me over," he'd say.

One piece of mail, however, we dreaded receiving. Fortunately it arrived very seldom, but when it did there wasn't one of us children who would remove it from the box. We would run to the house as fast as our legs would carry us, with our voices screaming even before we hit the kitchen, "Mother, go quickly to the mailbox. There's a letter edged in black." We knew it was a death notice: to us, it carried an ominous message, so we wanted nothing to do with it. The letters edged in black were sent to those families who, living a distance from relatives and long-time friends with no telephone, had no other way of being notified of a death.

But in most cases the mailman brought nothing but good, newsy letters and parcels. We thought he was just as important to our survival as the country doctor.

I also remember the mailman as being a kindly and concerned member of the community. Often he would stop to herd a cow, which had wandered on to the road, back into our pasture, or he would pitch a few forks of hay with my father as he worked in the field beside the road. And many was the time when he would pile two or three of us into the front of the buggy with the rest of us clinging to the back behind the seat. This was just to lessen our three-mile walk from the Northcote school.

It was to be expected, I'm sure. But, nonetheless, the day was a sad one when the mailman graduated from a horse and buggy to an old Chev car. In doing so, he drove on the wrong side of the road and completely changed his route. Now we could no longer see him coming round the gravel pit. He was often hours earlier than we expected. The excitement of seeing him draw closer to our mailbox vanished with the advent of this new method of transportation.

The mailman continued, however, to be our link with the world beyond Renfrew County. As children, we knew not how the mail made its magic trip from those far-off places; we only knew that, come hell or high water, what was destined for us was going to find its way magically into our mailbox.

THACKER'S GARAGE, OWNED BY CLIFTON THACKER, A VERY PROMINENT RENFREW BUSINESSMAN, WAS A FAVOURITE STOPPING PLACE. THE OLD BOX HEATER OFFERED A WARM SPOT ON A COLD DAY, AND MANY POLITICAL ISSUES WERE DISCUSSED BY THOSE WHO HABITUALLY MET THERE. THE DOOR WAS ALWAYS OPEN. (*PHOTO COURTESY OF CLARA THACKER.*)

To ride a bull

One day Cecil wandered into the yard from the Northcote road to see what we were up to. His bare feet were dusty and two big horse-blanket pins anchored his short pants to his shirt. "Can't find anything to do," was his first comment. Audrey reminded him that school had only been out a few weeks and that the long, hot summer still lay ahead.

Cecil sat on the wire gate and then immediately turned upside down, a favourite position of his. When he did this, his Adam's apple moved up and down his neck like a yo-yo. Even his ears seemed to hang down. Cecil was a strange one, all right.

"Eat barley and you'll choke, unless you can get a crow to peck the stock out," was his next comment. "And if you swallow choke cherries and drink milk at the same time, you'll die." I digested this information and decided right then and there that I would avoid barley and choke cherries for the rest of my days.

My three brothers and Audrey, my sister, listened to Cecil's comments but said nothing. "Say, we could play in the ice house," the upside-down boy offered. We assured him that a death by eating barley or choke cherries would be mild compared to the fate in store for us if we were caught in the ice house. We weren't even allowed in to get a block of ice for the old Barnett refrigerator until the sun had gone down, let alone to enter in broad daylight for a frolic.

Cecil continued to contemplate. "We could hitch old Harry to the hay fork and ride up into the mow." Old Harry was our horse with the heaves, who Father said wasn't long for this world. Cecil's ideas were getting crazier by the minute.

When he received no response to the hay fork idea, he said, "I'm bored silly. There's nothin' to do. I thought at least you guys would have something in mind." Audrey suggested we make up a play and put it on in the grape arbour. Cecil said this wasn't exactly what he had in mind.

Just then his eyes, which had started to bulge from him being in the upside-down position for so long, slid towards the cows in the barnyard. "Ever ridden a bull bare-back?" His Adam's apple was working frantically. Emerson told him we only tried this when the cows were tied in their stalls for milking. We all snorted and laughed at the prospect of anyone in his right mind trying to ride a bull bare-back.

Cecil dropped to the ground, whereupon the blood drained from his face and he returned to a normal colour. He jumped the fence, and all five of us lined up like pigeons on a rail waiting to see what he was going to do next.

Cecil approached Ben, who was licking the salt block. He looked as calm as a cucumber, but he could be mean. Cecil gave the bull's flanks a few, friendly slaps. Then, with one giant leap, he was on the bull's back with his bare legs digging into the bull's ribs.

It took a few seconds for Ben to realize what was happening. But, when he did, his two hind feet left the ground at exactly the same time.

Cecil slid down towards the bull's neck where only the two horns kept him from landing on the ground. He wrapped his arms around the bull's neck and hung on for dear life as old Ben bucked and bolted across the barnyard. Ben was tossing his head from left to right, and Cecil was screaming like mad, which further excited the animal. I put my hands over my eyes and opened two fingers just a smidgen to peek at the show in front of us.

After about five minutes of bucking about the barnyard, the bull came to an abrupt halt in front of the watering trough, and Cecil, grasping the only opportunity open to him, slid off its neck and jumped into the trough in one leap. The bull glared at him but, like the young rider, was exhausted from the ordeal.

Cecil climbed out of the trough backwards, never taking his eyes off the bull for a second, and made for the fence against which we were all leaning. This time Cecil opened the gate and walked into the yard towards the lane. He was rubbing his seat. "Well, guess I'll wander home," he said. "Sure wish we could find something to do around here. It's going to be a long summer."

Our mother, the author

My mother used to spend hours working on her books. One book was a financial record of every penny earned and spent on our Renfrew County farm during the thirties. It was a ledger between whose covers no one ever saw. When she was making entries, Mother's face wore a worried look, and my brothers, sister, and I would barely glance her way. But we would steal a peak only when her writing was punctuated with long, calculated sighs of despair. When Mother was finished with the ledger, she would snap it shut and, with her fingers drumming on the table oilcloth, she would sit for a long time looking into the depths of the dimly lit kitchen.

This book of doom — as we got to calling it — was symbolically bound in black.

Mother's diaries, too, consumed many of her evening hours. While she was writing in them, her face wore a look of intense concentration, and every so often she would pause, stare at one of us, smile, and then write furiously in the diary. At the time, we were never sure why we inspired her diary prose: we only knew that she got great pleasure out of what she wrote between the covers. The books grew in number until she had about ten of them, whose contents spanned the years we lived on the farm.

But the book she probably enjoyed most was one she called, simply enough, her storybook. This was our favourite as well because she shared with us what was written inside.

The stories were pure fiction, according to our mother. But when she read them to us we often found we had been woven into the yarns. Some of the incidents were quite familiar. Mother wrote at great lengths about the farm and a family she named the Ditwells who, surprisingly enough, also had five children and two city cousins, who spent a great deal of time on the farm. However, our mother neglected to turn one of the cousins into an incorrigible character like Ronny. The stories depicted the two boys as sweet, young things, shy of the farm animals and, as I recall now, both cousins were sickly. The various diseases gave Mother ample opportunity to expound on the virtues of home-grown remedies and cures.

Occasionally she would be especially happy with the way in which one of the stories developed. She would spend many a night at the kitchen table, polishing the piece of fiction, changing a word here and a phrase there. She would then test the story on us and carefully monitor our responses. If we laughed when we should have cried, she would pause in mid-sentence, take a black crayon, and underline the offending or questionable phrase. These corrections went on until she had perhaps rewritten the story a dozen times.

Then, when it was letter-perfect in her estimation, she would make one final copy on white notepaper using a 'nib' pen. This copy went into a long envelope, and she would lick the flap shut and press it to her lips with eyes closed. And we knew she was deep in silent prayer. At the time we didn't know to whom she was mailing the stories. Once, my brother Emerson said he thought perhaps it was God because she never sent one off without praying over it. Mother gave us not a clue, even when we questioned her: she would merely scoff and say, "Oh, no one in particular" or "You wouldn't know the party."

One Saturday night, as usual, we were all sitting round the old pine table in the kitchen and taking turns playing our Eaton's catalogue game and browsing through the *Philadelphia Enquirer*, which was bought weekly with our supplies in Renfrew. Our mother threw her hands in the air and, with her eyes to the heavens, said, "Dear Mary, mother of God." We were terrified because that prayer was usually reserved for some terrible calamity. But Mother was flushed scarlet and glowing like a beacon light. "It's here, right here in the *Philadelphia Enquirer*. My story has been published. See, it says 'Life with the Ditwells, by Mabel Haneman'." We tore round to her end of the table and even Father, who was slow to rouse, sauntered over from the rocking chair near the Findlay Oval — but taking the time to light his pipe first. There before our very eyes was our mother's name in print. We begged her to read it to us so that we could all enjoy it at the same time. With a trembling voice, she read her story but with such emphasis that she could have been a stand-in for Sarah Bernhardt. When she was finished, Mother's eyes were full of tears and Father was muttering something about if she was going to be that upset from seeing her name in print she would be wise not to send off any more stories. We paid him no heed but ran our fingers over the heading where her name was and marvelled at our mother, the author.

We tried to order extra copies of the *Philadelphia Enquirer*. Of course, we were the only people in Renfrew County who bought the paper, which was brought in every Saturday by Fraser & Smart drug store especially for our mother. So we had to make do with the one copy. The article was carefully clipped out of the paper and placed between tissue sheets in our mother's story-book. In the evenings, when her books were out in front of her, we would see her reading over the story that had been printed in the American newspaper. And we marvelled again at the thousands of people who would have read the story of 'Life with the Ditwells', written by our mother, the author.

MY MOTHER, THE AUTHOR

Raspberry picking with the bear

Across the fields from our house and barns was a thick bush. In the early spring it provided us with a clear, white sap that we boiled into syrup; it gave up thick hardwood that burned all winter. And deep in its very heart was the raspberry patch, the nicest place of all on the farm. My father would check the berry bush often, and when he thought the raspberries were ready for picking, ''Operation Raspberry'' would go into full swing.

It started with my mother scouring out about six large milk cans — the kind that sell in the antique stores today for up to sixty dollars . Each of us had big straw hats to which hoods of green netting were secured to keep off the mosquitoes. Enough food for our lunches was packed to feed a battalion because we would be at the raspberry patch for the entire day. My father always took the rifle along. We thought this was ridiculous because, as far as we were concerned, no harm could come to us back in the bush. But Mother said she felt safer with the gun; however, she would never tell us of what she was frightened.

We would go back to the patch on the small wagon. On our way to the bush we would sing songs with our mother accompanying us on her harmonica. The whole trip there and back would have a party atmosphere, and we all looked forward to the expedition with great anticipation.

When we reached the clearing, just before the raspberry bushes started, it was as if we had entered another world. Big, red, sweet berries hung like jewels from the prickly bushes. I know I will have to be a lot older than I am now before the picture of those branches heavy with fruit, and the peace and quietness of the bush, fades from my memory.

All of us, from the eldest to the youngest, worked methodically. We fanned out and worked a section at a time: as the little honey pails with the wire handles, which were tied around our waists, were filled, we went to the central spot and gently, oh so gently, poured the plump berries into the milk cans.

Now Mother, having come from the city, had a healthy respect for the deep bush. No one was allowed to move out of her sight. We sang songs to keep in touch, and every so often there would be a head count to make sure all seven of us were accounted for.

The year I remember best was the year we were all grateful that Father had taken along the gun.

We had tired of the singing and were picking silently — each with his own thoughts. Suddenly, my father, with barely a whisper, said, "Quiet, don't anyone move. Stay perfectly still right where you are." We froze. Even the picking stopped as we heard the dry twigs break and the rustle of leaves on the forest bed behind us. I wanted so badly to run to either my father or my mother, but the command to stay perfectly still stopped me.

The steps came closer and closer and, even though the heat of the day was upon us, I felt a chill as if it were the middle of winter. Then into the clearing came the first bear I had ever seen in my life. The terror on my mother's face sent a panic through me, but I dared not move. I realized our lives depended on doing exactly what we had been told. I saw Father take the gun from the strap across his back. He did it so slowly that he was almost motionless. The bear looked at us one at a time; he sniffed the milk cans, now almost full of berries; then he wandered over to the lunch. His grunts of satisfaction told us he was enjoying something from the picnic basket. Still we didn't move. Then, as nonchalantly as he had come, the bear turned with not another look and went back into the bush. My father never fired a shot.

We continued picking for the rest of the day — but not without furtive glances behind us. Never again did we question our father when he insisted that the rifle be part of our raspberry picking gear.

Lessons on character-building

Marguerite and her mother drove into our yard one Saturday morning. The dust of the road clouded around them when they stopped at the house, attesting to the long, dry spell we were experiencing that summer. Already the sun was relentlessly beating down on us. Mother had the doors shut tight and the quilts over the windows to keep out the hot rays.

Marguerite was more excited than usual, and the girl that I could barely tolerate in school jumped from the car before her mother had it stopped. Her golden curls were in disarray from the breeze of the open car, but she still managed to look as if she had just stepped out of the pages of a city magazine. She always wore little, white bobby sox with flowers embroidered around the tops, and her white, leather-strapped shoes had just been polished. I felt more conscious than ever of my bare feet.

I knew that I was feeling jealous, but Marguerite did little to make me feel differently. She constantly showed off her new clothes or a new doll bought when it wasn't even Christmas or a birthday. Often she had a few coins knotted in the corner of her handkerchief, which she carried tucked into the wristband of a real watch that ticked and told time. I thought at the time that Marguerite was the luckiest girl in the Valley. As she was an only child, her parents catered to her every whim; in our large, boisterous family, it was every man for himself.

Marguerite's mother had come to ask if I could go with her daughter to a camp that had been advertised in the *Ottawa Farm Journal*. It was to be for a week, and there were real cabins to sleep in, not tents like we had at church camp. This camp was being held on the Ottawa River, miles from our farm. It would only cost five dollars for the week. I would need running shoes, the woman said, as she looked with obvious disgust at my dusty, bare feet.

I weighed the pros and cons of going off to camp for a full week with Marguerite. But the more I heard about the venture, the more I accepted that I could put up with her antics for a short time. Besides, even though we were strong competitors in school, we still played together a lot on Saturdays.

I couldn't understand why Mother didn't jump at the chance to send me to this marvellous camp. She was most hesitant and finally said she would have to discuss it with Father when he came in for noon dinner. She would ring up later in the day to let them know. That was as good as saying 'yes' to me, and Marguerite and I danced around the yard with excitement.

In another cloud of dust Marguerite and her mother were gone. With a renewed burst of friendliness, I waved at the car until it was out of sight. Mother had gone into the house, closing the door quickly so as not to let in any heat. I did likewise as I rushed in to talk about the week at camp.

Then, without any warning, Mother said — and I thought her voice had caught — "You know you can't go, Mary." I felt as if someone had hit me hard in the stomach. "It's not fair that your brothers and sister can't go, and we certainly don't have five dollars to spare. That's a lot of money." I thought to myself that, if she mentions one more time there's a Depression on, I'm going to scream loud enough to be heard in Admaston. But Mother didn't. "We just don't have the money, you know. And you'd have to have new running shoes, and you certainly couldn't take that old bathing suit Aunt Lizzie sent in the hand-me-down box. It's about four sizes too big. So we'd have to go to Walker's in Renfrew and buy a new one, and there would go another two dollars." Her voice trailed off.

I had sunk into a chair in the darkened room, and I could feel my eyes begin to brim with tears. I asked if perhaps we couldn't wait until Father came in for dinner before making up our minds. Mother said it would make no difference as he had no magic formula for producing five dollars either. I told her I could contribute twelve cents: I had had it in my dresser drawer since the last Renfrew Fair. But Mother said I'd need to come up with much more than that. I didn't move out of the chair all morning, waiting for Father.

When he came into the kitchen to wash up, I flew to him to hand him the soap and hold the roller towel out from the wall. He knew instantly that I was busting to tell him something. But Mother had beaten me to it. Father's face was expressionless. "Well, if we haven't got the money, we haven't got the money."

He did not say anything after that, but walked to the kitchen table and his dinner.

There was no point in trying to continue the discussion. The matter was closed. It was one of the rare times I was excused from eating — and I rushed out to the grape arbour where I cried for almost an hour.

When I came into the house later, Mother was just hanging up the receiver and ringing off. I only heard her last words, "Thank you, and I'm sorry."

Mother wrung out a face cloth with cold well water and passed it over my eyes, which were almost swollen shut from crying. She talked about there being other times, and that perhaps we could pitch the tent on the Bonnechere like we did last summer. And then she talked about every disappointment being a character-builder. During those lean years in Renfrew County I felt I had enough character-building to last me a lifetime.

WHAT IS THIS NEW ABODE
WHEREIN I FIND MYSELF SO SUDDENLY?
WITH SPACES AS WIDE AS THE CITY I LEFT BEHIND.
I LOOK ACROSS THE FIELDS AND THE HILLS,
AND WONDER WHY I AM HERE.
AND THEN I SEE THE LIVES WHO REACH OUT FOR MY HAND,
AND MY ANSWER COMES
AS SURELY AS THE BLOSSOMS ON THE VINE.

— MABEL ERNESTINE LAPOINTE

Patrick Herman

Although many of the residents of the community in which we lived were either Lutherans or United Church supporters, there were a few Roman Catholics as well. Most of them were either Irish or German families who had originally settled in the Mount St. Patrick area. I can't remember there being many prejudices against the Catholics during the thirties, but certainly we knew there was a difference between Protestants and Roman Catholics.

In my own family, my Lutheran father never let my mother, a Catholic, forget that he thought her leanings were more than a bit odd. And when he was talking about someone who belonged to ***that church***, he would add, "He's a Catholic, you know," as if the poor soul was infirm. Father also insisted that every Catholic he ever knew had a violent temper. This was sheer nonsense, naturally. For instance, we always thought our mother was more even tempered than many Lutherans we knew — with one exception.

Patrick Herman would fight at the drop of a hat. He was a German — and a Catholic. And he was a great friend of my brother Earl, with whom he often came home after school to play. Nothing was ever said in front of the lad by my father about his religion, but he often wondered how a German family from good stock had ended up in the Catholic church.

Now, when it came to my brother Emerson, that was a different story. He loved to tease Patrick Herman about the medal he wore around his neck, the beads that were in his pocket with his jack-knife and sling-shot, and his refusal to eat meat when he visited our house on a Friday. Although Mother had given up most of the Catholic customs when she married a Lutheran, whenever Patrick Herman came to visit on a Friday, she fixed him a big omelette while the rest of us had meat.

We always thought that Father's mealtime graces were much longer when Patrick Herman was visiting. One time Mother even accused Father of praying at length just to aggravate our young visitor, who sat silently with his eyes closed and crossed himself periodically.

One Friday Patrick Herman came home from school with Earl. He was to stay the night and go bullfrog hunting on the Bonnechere the next morning. We all played together after chores. Then it was time to go into the summer kitchen to wash up. Our guest was first, and with Emerson he moved towards the table to make room for the many other pairs of hands waiting for the wash-basin. My brother had been teasing Patrick Herman all afternoon, and Mother had already told him twice to hush up.

But Emerson had to get in just one more lick. ''Hey, everybody! Patrick Herman just ate a piece of sausage from the frying pan, and it's Friday.'' ''I did not, you Luthern liar,'' Patrick Herman shot back. And the fight was on.

They rolled on the floor, jabbing away at each other until Mother pulled Emerson away by the ear. Patrick Herman was still flailing at the air long after the fight had halted.

When we finally got settled around the pine table, the fight appeared to have been forgotten and Patrick Herman dug into the omelette as heartily as we dug into the sausages. But come bedtime, Mother held Emerson back, and we could hear her lecturing him below us. We could also hear Father making a few snorts through his nose as he always did when he was scoffing. He even commented on the silliness of calling a boy by two first names. Mother said this had nothing to do with the issue and that if she ever heard Emerson making fun of Patrick Herman again he would have her to deal with.

I wish I could say that this incident ended the teasing. But it didn't. Emerson just moved his performance out of earshot. Now that I think of it though, we Lutherans took a fair amount of ribbing from the United Church goers too. But when it came to things that were truly important, religion made no difference. No one stopped to think what church you went to when it came thrashing time, or if a farmer needed help in building a barn. Those Renfrew County people worked together and played together. Yet, it was surely that great binder of neighbours, the Depression, that lifted all of them above any religious prejudices.

The hired man

Tommy Roher was a strange, little man who wandered in one day off the Northcote road, looking for a job. He was what was known as a home boy, having come over from England with hundreds of other young orphans to work on the farms in the Ottawa Valley. Many of them, like Tommy, left the farms to which they had been sent because of mistreatment and joined countless tramps roaming the back roads in search of a warm bed and food for their bellies.

My father had made it clear that there would be no salary as such. Tommy would have a place to sleep and plenty to eat, we'd buy his cigarettes when we had the money to spare and, if a few dollars could occasionally be squeezed out of our meagre farm income, he would get a bit to meet his barest needs.

The arrangements seemed to suit Tommy just fine, and he soon became part of our family. But he was quiet, and all the time he was with us we learned little about his background. He wore a hurt in his eyes that time couldn't erase, and the rare times he smiled were like respites during a bad storm.

Tommy had been with us several years when my father noticed he was becoming restless. He did his chores as well as ever, but we often caught him looking at a spot in the corner of the kitchen with such an intensity that we wondered if he saw something we didn't. Father would say under his breath, "He's a million miles away is Tommy." In the evenings he would go off to his own little corner in the back kitchen, and no amount of coaxing could lure him into a game of cards or a sing-song.

Then one night when we women of the house — my mother, my sister, and I — were readying the kitchen and the brothers were deep into a game of Snakes and Ladders, we heard Tommy say to Father in his soft voice, "I think it's time I moved on." Everything stopped as quick as a wink: Mother's hands stopped swishing the dishrag in the pan, Audrey stopped drying, and so quickly did I turn around on the chair on which I was standing that, had I not grabbed hold of the kitchen pump, I would have lost my balance. We all stared at Tommy, who looked as if he was going to cry.

Father was the first to break the deadly silence. "And where might you be going, Tommy?" "Well", said Tommy, "I hear they are looking for a man down a side road," and he named a farmer we knew well. We knew him because he was a scoundrel, and his reputation as a skin-flint was common knowledge in our parts.

We children flew to the little man who had been such a part of our lives for so many years and begged him to stay. I offered to give him the few pennies I had tucked into the corner of my dresser drawer upstairs, and Emerson surprised us all by volunteering to do Tommy's chores in the mornings so that he could sleep in. But Tommy, it seemed, had made up his mind. He would drive over with the horse and buggy in the morning and see if he could strike up a bargain with the farmer who lived across the Bonnechere River. We again started to protest loudly, but Father raised his hand and we knew the matter was closed.

The next day my stomach felt as if it was weighted down with cement. While we sat at the supper table Tommy said he would be leaving at the end of the week. We children couldn't do enough for him, reasoning that if we smothered him with kindness he would change his mind.

But Saturday night came and Tommy took two brown, paper bags from the rack in the kitchen and escaped into his back room. When he came out, he had on his best trousers, a plaid shirt that at one time belonged to my father, and a tie we had given him the year before for Christmas. Everything he owned was in the two bags. With promises that he would see us all often and a handshake for my mother, he went into the night with my father to be driven over to the farmer's homestead.

The house wore a gloom I had never witnessed before. Not that Tommy added much joy and sunlight to the atmosphere, but we thought of him as family and we couldn't bear any break in the unit. We missed having him at the supper table, rumpling our hair as he passed our chairs, and his soft "goodnight" to us as we climbed the stairs. But our mother told us as time wore on we would fret less and less.

By Monday morning, none of us felt any better and we took off out the lane, dragging our feet. The day was endless. It was dark when we got home from the three-and-a-half mile walk to the Northcote school, and the lamp in the window did little to cheer us. But when we opened the door, we could smell cigarette smoke and we saw Tommy's old windbreaker hanging on the hook at the stove. We dropped our books in the middle of the floor and charged into the back room where Tommy was unpacking the two brown, paper bags he had taken with him just two days before. He talked more that night than he ever had before. "He was a mean one all right, and I didn't like the way he treated the horses either."

Later we sang songs, and Tommy even joined in for a chorus or two. When it was time for us to go up the stairs to bed and leave the adults to a few minutes of private talk, Tommy surveyed the kitchen as if he had never seen it before. And then he said in his soft, British voice, "It' sure good to be home."

MOTHER CAPTURES A VISITING COUSIN, TOMMY ROHER, EVERETT AND EMERSON ON THE HORSES, EARL, AND ME.

Father's first airplane ride

"God never planned that my feet should be above the trees when I'm gettin' from one place to the other,'' Father would say when anyone asked him if he would like to go up in an airplane. In the first place, he had no use for modern contraptions. It was years before he switched to a tractor to do the plowing—and then only because he got a good deal on a trade.

Of all the new-fangled inventions, the airplane was the worst in Father's mind. Emerson, who was the most mechanical in the family, tried to explain the theory behind air currents, but Father refused to discuss what he considered a useless exercise. He had absolutely no intention of ever putting his feet higher than the floor boards of the old Model T.

Not surprisingly, when Emerson won a trip over the town of Renfrew in a plane, Father was less than pleased. My brother, on the other hand, was ecstatic. How he won has long since faded from my mind: I think it had something to do with collecting empty bottles of 'Kik' at Briscoe's store.

Emerson was excited beyond belief the day we all loaded into the car to drive to a field outside the fair grounds in Renfrew for the free ride. A much more adventurous person than Father, Mother thought this was the most exciting thing to happen to the family since we got the telephone. She kept patting Emerson's knee all the way into Renfrew as if he had just won some major science prize in a competition.

The little plane sat like a Praying Mantis in the hay field. It didn't look as if it was going anywhere. Dozens of spectators were standing around: we soon discovered that Emerson wasn't the only one who had won a free ride. When the pilot started the motor, the grass was blown flat and the roar drowned out all conversation. Emerson's eyes resembled dinner plates when he saw the plane with its first passenger careen down the field, hitting the ruts and hay hobbles as it went. The plane circled the field twice and then came in for a bumpy landing, grinding to a halt just yards from where we stood.

It was then that we saw the young boy, not much older than Emerson, fall out of the seat and promptly throw up at the side of the airplane. He walked crazily towards his mother, who was standing right beside us. "It was terrible," he groaned between heaves. "I've never been so scared."

Now Emerson was a big boy — big for his age — and he was tough. Not much frightened him. But he couldn't stand seeing anyone being sick. Before long he was heaving in the hay field too — and he hadn't even been near the plane.

Emerson's name was called next, but my brother flatly refused to move from the spot to which he was riveted. Mother was getting annoyed, and Father was lamenting that Emerson was depriving someone who was more deserving of a trip. The organizers tried to force Emerson into the little door of the plane, but he planted both feet against the door jambs. He wouldn't budge. The pilot had his head out the window and said he was going up, with or without the next passenger.

The next thing we knew, Father had grabbed the slip of paper out of Emerson's hand and was climbing into the passenger's seat. The door slammed behind him, and then we saw the plane bobbing across the hay field. Mother could only say, "Holy Mary, Mother of God."

The flight lasted only a few minutes. Father sprang from the plane as if his flight aloft was an everyday occurrence. Emerson started to cry: his stomach had settled and he wanted to go up. But it was too late. The trip pass had been used.

On the way back to the farm, Father said the ride was the most exciting thing that had ever happened to him. He couldn't imagine how anyone could be afraid of flying. This didn't sound like the same man who had lamented all the way to Renfew that anyone who left the ground in one of those machines had to be demented.

Father talked about his experience for weeks. He even told the farmers after church the next Sunday, and the next time we were at Briscoe's store we saw him looking over the display of 'Kik' bottles to see if the contest was still on. Father even went so far as to say he might consider ***paying*** for a ride if the occasion ever presented itself again.

Little girls and dolls

As a little girl growing up on the farm, no other pastime gave me greater pleasure than playing with my dolls. In spite of the lack of money for such frivolous things as new dolls, I seemed to have had a better array than many of my more affluent friends. Oh, without a doubt Joyce and Marguerite had bigger and better-dressed dolls as theirs probably came from a big store in Ottawa. My dolls had been handed down to me from my older sister. One that Mother owned when she was a little girl I was especially fond of.

In my memories I can picture two dolls that came from Aunt Lizzie in Regina. They came either wrapped in an old man's suit or stuffed into the arm of a boy's sweater that would no longer fit her two sons. Since she had no daughters, I suppose she had bought the dolls to send to me, no doubt knowing that there would be little money for such luxuries as a new doll.

One doll she sent I remember very well. It had a china face and china arms and legs with round balls for elbow and knee joints. I handled it with the respect due a fine china doll and dressed and undressed it with the utmost care. I remember this doll had tiny, blue eyes with lashes, and the eyes closed whenever I put it down to sleep.

I had several dolls with soft, straw-stuffed bodies, too. One of them had a little box embedded in its back, which allowed it to cry when it was turned upside down. My brother Emerson, who I considered hateful at the time, removed the box one day to see how it worked — and it was if someone had mutilated my own heart. I cried for hours, and Mother, after dealing with him severely in the wood-shed, tried to patch it up as best she could. However, from then on the doll cried when it sat up and did nothing when laid down, as it was supposed to.

I also loved a little, black doll passionately. As it was made of very hard composition, the doll wasn't at all cuddly, which was my preference. But, nonetheless, it was an important part of my family of dolls.

In those days, of course, dolls' clothes were not sold in the stores. The dolls came in simple, little dresses, and it was up to you to supply them with their own wardrobes. Mother, never to lose an opportunity that could be turned into a learning experience, would have my sister and I cut out patterns from brown paper, fit them to the doll, and then cut clothes from scraps of material. It was a special delight if you could have a doll dressed in the same piece of gingham you wore to school. I was never allowed to use the old, footpedal Singer sewing machine, though Audrey was. This I considered a grave injustice. Mother would make me thread a needle and sew by hand all the dolls' clothes she had painstakingly helped me cut out.

I would never go to bed at night without first putting all my dolls in the little, blue crib Father had made for me one Christmas. When winter came, I would place the crib close to the stovepipe so that the dolls wouldn't get cold during the night. First thing every morning I checked to see if they had survived. I can remember insisting to everyone that one or two of them had stirred while I was asleep. Emerson, of course, would go into great spasms of laughter at this suggestion.

In fact, I used to believe the dolls were so real that I wouldn't say one bad thing about any of them when they were within earshot. Once, when the paint wore off one of the plaster faces, I can remember whispering to Mother that the doll was very sick and would probably die — but I made sure at the time that I was well away from the crib where the doll was. And when a doll would eventually succumb to the gruelling routine of constant fondling, I would be inconsolable. Mother, waiting until I wasn't around, would then dispose of the doll.

As I preferred dolls that looked like babies, I had no desire to own a doll with bouffant hair and party dresses. They were impossible to mother and so had no place in my heart.

Looking back now on those years during the Depression, I realize there weren't too many things a little girl could play with other than dolls. We had no easy-bake-ovens, or small electric irons, or crafts, or games with flashing lights. Our entertainment was of the simplest kind: home-made doll houses, cribs made of scraps of wood, scrap-books, simple board games, skipping rope made from braided binder twine, home-made sleighs and skis, and dolls.

Dolls allowed a little girl to escape into a world of make-believe. This was a world where material wealth had no meaning:

when holding or tucking one of those precious dolls into its crib at night, a poor girl could, for a moment, be just like any other little girl in the world who was born to riches and privileges.

MY THREE BROTHERS, RONNY AND TERRY WITH THEIR SHAVED HEADS, AND ME WITH ONE OF MY FAVOURITE DOLLS.

A Saturday night on the town

My brothers felt secure with a few coins rattling around in their pockets. No one could know that these probably consisted of just a few pennies, augmented by a couple of nails and sometimes small discs of metal retrieved from the drive-shed. When the boys weren't working around the farm at the dozens of chores they were expected to do each day, they wore what we called 'dress breeks'. These had ample legs that ended at the lower part of the knee and were cuffed with a button. They also had deep side pockets. My brothers had a habit of walking around with their hands thrust deep in these pockets, their fingers playing with the few coins and various other metal objects, which created the illusion of abundant wealth.

The boys especially liked to rattle their pockets when they were walking the main street of Renfrew on a Saturday night while our parents were at Scott's Hardware or the Fraser & Smart drug store. Mother made them wear white shirts, ties, and wide tweed caps, which Emerson insisted on pulling jauntily over one eye. This Mother thought was coarse because those town roughnecks wore their caps this way. Naturally, the jaunty angle became more appealing than ever.

Dressed in their next-to-best finery, the three brothers would go up and down Raglan Street, rolling the metal in their pockets. In this way, the boys hoped to attract everyone's attention to the fact that, just because they lived out in the country, was no reason to suspect they were penniless.

Everett and Earl took their cue from Emerson who, on spotting a group of boys standing near a street light, would saunter up within touching distance, pause to look up at the light, and rattle his pockets. The three of them would hover around for a few minutes, each fondling his coins and other objects, and then move away down the street, convinced that they had given those town boys something to think about.

My brothers did the same thing when they went into the dime store, which was a favourite place to spend a good hour on a Saturday night. A huge strap of a lad, Emerson would walk right to where the pipes were laid out in neat rows: there were dozens of them of every shape and size, some with curved stems and some with carved bowls. Although he had no intention of buying a pipe because he didn't have enough money and because Mother wouldn't allow him to smoke one, Emerson would handle the pipes as if he knew exactly what made each one a good smoke.

Audrey and I knew perfectly well what took him and my two brothers to the pipe counter. This was the perfect place to impress the young high school girl with long, golden ringlets who had a Saturday job in the dime store. She would stand shyly behind the counter while the three brothers talked with an air of authority about the various pipes and which ones they were considering buying. And all the time they would be rattling the coins and various other pieces of metal in their pockets to give the impression that there wasn't a pipe on the counter, even the one that sold for $1.99, that wasn't within their reach if they so desired. Audrey and I were appalled at this blatant show of trickery but knew better than to expose the little game as we would have paid dearly when we got back to the farm.

After they had impressed as many people as possible along the main street of Renfrew, the boys would wander back down to Thacker's Garage where the car was parked. Here they would move out of the beam of the street light and pull the coins from their pockets. They would count out the pennies each had to see if they could pool them together and perhaps come up with enough to go into the drug store and buy an ice cream cone. As they usually had just enough money for one cone, one brother was delegated to make the purchase. Then the three of them would sit on the front bumper of the car and take turns licking it.

During the next week, they would accumulate another small pile of coins by selling produce or doing odd jobs on the next farm. Once again, then, they would head into Renfrew with their breeks' pockets full. And only we would know that a small portion of the contents was money.

The grand clash

One of my favourite pastimes — like every other little girl I knew — was dressing and undressing my dolls. I spent hours sitting in the grape arbour or on the old, wooden swing and clothing them in the variety of clothes my mother and older sister had made for me out of flour bags and scraps of print.

Ronny, that impish cousin from Montreal who spent most of his young life on the farm with us, prided himself on his grown-up manliness. He considered even a sidelong glance at a doll to be sissy and damaging to his reputation as a force with which to be reckoned. My brother Emerson who was just a few years older than Ronny, often teamed up with him, and together they performed many a dastardly deed that put the entire homestead in turmoil.

On our farm there was one barn cat of which I was especially fond. Actually, she was the only cat I liked. The others were always scrapping, and I developed a healthy respect for them. But Whitey was the one barn cat that ventured closest to the house without passing the point where she was not allowed — because Mother had a strict rule that absolutely no cat was allowed indoors.

One day my dolls, Emerson and Ronny, and Whitey all came together in one glorious clash that sent the two boys to the wood-shed to be dealt with by Father, me climbing the elm tree to escape the war on the ground, and Whitey taking a fit and running to the hayloft, not to emerge until days later. Mother had washed that day, so it must have been a Monday as it was unheard of to wash clothes on any other day.

I can remember sitting with my dolls under the old elm tree, and I must have dressed and undressed them a dozen times. Emerson and Ronny were swinging on the old, wood swing a few paces away, and it was obvious they were plotting some terrible deed. Whitey, who had found a cool spot a few feet from the well, was out flat like a white and black pillow. The boys were looking at me, and then at Whitey, all the time talking in whispers.

Emerson asked to borrow some of my doll's clothes, a request that was even more strange than usual. Of course, I flatly refused. Both boys slid off the swing. One went to the clothes-line, the other snaked over to Whitey. I saw Ronny unpin some of the clean, dry clothes from the line, while Emerson pounced on Whitey, who stiffened as if she had been given an electric shock. He carried her screeching all the way to the swing.

Ronny had my flour-bag bloomers, one of Mother's small fancy aprons, and my sister's brassière in his hand, as well as a pair of short, white bobby sox, which belonged to my younger cousin Terry. Whitey was upside down on Emerson's lap, and Ronny was feeding her limbs into the garments. The bloomers went on without a hitch, but the brassière had to be wrapped under her two or three times. The boys shoved Whitey's front legs into one sock and her back legs into the other. The small apron, Mother's finest hand-embroidered one reserved for Sundays, was put cape style around the cat's neck.

I stared transfixed, secretly wishing the cat would bite them, but Emerson and Ronny had too good a grip on her. Once they had all the clothes on, they dropped her to the ground where she rolled over several times trying to find her balance. But the bobby sox were a hinderance, and she fought to free herself. The apron covered her back like an organza shawl, and the white cotton brassière looked like it actually belonged where the boys had put it.

Whitey circled the yard about three times before she finally lost the sox. Mother's best apron was filthy, and it looked very much like Audrey's brassière would go to the grave with Whitey. Ronny and Emerson were rolling on the ground laughing. By this time Whitey was frantic, but before making for the barn she circled the yard one more time and attacked Sport, our collie, who had done nothing more than raise his head to watch the performance. It was obvious the cat was having a fit. Sport slashed at her with his paw, and the fight was on. When it was over, the apron was in ribbons, but the brassière was still anchored around the cat's body.

Mother came out of the summer kitchen in time to see her organza apron go through the cow-byre door. She got hold of Ronny and Emerson by the ears and dragged them into the woodshed where they were ordered to stay until Father came home for his lunch. Upon being told about her brassière, Audrey offered to go to the back field and fetch Father home at once. Mother assured her the strapping could wait.

We never knew if Father got around to punishing the boys. By the time Mother, Audrey, and I finished telling him the whole story, he was wiping the tears from his eyes and slapping the side of his leg. He did promise to go to the wood-shed immediately, however, and deal with the issue. But I strongly suspect the three of them sat on the woodpile for the best part of an hour until Father regained his composure. When they came out, he tried to look stern, and the boys did their best to look contrite. But it was obvious to the rest of us that the old maple switch had not been used that day.

A FAVOURITE PASTIME FOR MY ASSORTED COUSINS, BROTHERS, AND SISTER, AUDREY, WAS TO CRAWL ALL OVER A LOVED UNCLE AND GENERALLY CAVORT ON THE FRONT LAWN. EMERSON, SECOND FROM THE RIGHT, AS USUAL CLOWNS IN FRONT OF MOTHER'S CAMERA.

Turnips and the family way

I had long since abandoned the idea that girls could get in the family way simply by having a boy put his hand on their knee. Until then, however, this bit of misinformation caused me a great deal of concern for years, and I went out of my way to avoid as much physical contact with the opposite sex as I could manage.

A new fear about the cause of premature pregnancy resulted from a misunderstood comment and an over-active mind, which seemed to plague me most of my young life.

It all started when a chance remark by my oldest brother had me convinced that eating too many turnips was yet another way young girls could head down the path to disgrace.

A neighbour of ours in Renfrew County had a grand total of sixteen children. They were good neighbours, and some of the children, whose ages ranged from late twenties right down to babies on their mother's knee, were schoolmates at various times. Needless to say, they were the butt of many neighbourhood jokes, which annoyed my mother to no end. Although she often said there was absolutely no excuse for bringing that many children into the world during a Depression, she flatly refused to laugh at any of the remarks aimed at the couple about their large family.

However, although Mother heartily disapproved, my brothers could hardly wait to get in the door to tell Father the latest bit of humour they had heard about the parents down the road. Most of the comments went completely over my head, although I must admit my sister, Audrey, and I took everything in with the greatest concentration. Then we would sit upstairs in the bedroom we shared and, in whispers so that our mother wouldn't overhear, discussed at length the meaning of what had been said.

Like the children of today, we were preoccupied with the subject of reproduction: we were anxious to add to our vast storage of misinformation any way we could. Our hired man, for instance, said the large family had something to do with the fact that their house was a stone's throw from the railroad crossing. No doubt because he blew the whistle during the night and woke up the parents, Tom the engineer was in no small way responsible for the sixteen children. Try as we might, Audrey and I could ***not*** figure that one out.

The other bit of misinformation that stuck in our minds was a chance comment made by Velma's older brother. As Velma was my best friend and came from a devout Lutheran family, I figured her brother wouldn't dare make a comment that wasn't the gospel truth. He told us on the way to school one day, as we walked along the Northcote road where we always met up with the large family of children, that he knew exactly how the sixteen children came about. He was talking to my brother, so Audrey and I knew the information was not meant for our ears. He drove Everett a poke in the ribs that sent him reeling and said it had something to do with the long, cold, Renfrew winter nights. Audrey and I went through months of anguish trying to figure what this meant. We finally decided the best way to protect ourselves was to keep very warm when we went to bed. So for that entire winter we wore our long underwear under our nightgowns as added protection.

This huge family raised pigs. To help feed them, they grew acres of turnips — more than anyone else in the community. We passed these fields on the way to school. As if the reproduction of this large family was the most important issue of the day, my brother Emerson developed still another theory. He was convinced it was the turnips. He went on to explain that many was the time he had terrible gas pains after eating turnips; he also commented how our mother certainly thought they were good only for pig feed. Emerson said any fool could figure out that this vegetable was completely responsible for the family of sixteen children.

Well, this solution seemed the most logical to Audrey and me. And we couldn't imagine why we hadn't figured it out before because we both remembered having had stomach pains after a big feed of turnips. Needless to say, we avoided the vegetable like the Russian plague whenever our mother served it in the future. Audrey even toyed with the idea of mentioning the discovery to the oldest girl in the large family — so convinced were we that we had stumbled on to a great scientific discovery. It was probably fortunate for all of us that the family abruptly stopped growing at sixteen — for whatever reason, we knew not.

Father's daily routine

Although Father never complained of what must have been a boring day-to-day routine on the farm, it's difficult to imagine now how such repetition could produce anything but profound monotony and frustration. As with every other farmer we knew, Father's days changed only with the season.

He rose early when it was always dark, and if we wakened we could hear him padding around the house downstairs in his heavy wool socks. The sounds of his morning routine never varied. I could lie in bed upstairs and picture every move he made. To the wash-basin, to the mirror that hung over the bench at the back door, then the opening of the reservoir for warm water to shave, his straight razor slapping across the strap, which hung near the cupboard, then the scraping of the stove lids as he laid kindling to start the fire, the dipper reaching deep in the pail to fill the porridge pot.

His breakfast, likewise, never varied. Father usually liked to make his own. Once he was well into his hot gruel, he would take the time to come to the foot of the stairs and give two or three loud claps with his hands. This was our alarm clock. Mother would already be dressed and in the kitchen and, although she would try to chat, Father's replies were no more than the occasional agreement. I also noticed that Father was prone to long, calculated sighs in the early morning. Undaunted, Mother would ramble on about things, such as what was to be done with the garden, and that the Eaton's order should soon be in, or that next week it would be time to make apple cider. On reflection, I once again am aware of the tremendous differences in their personalities and dispositions.

Although we as children did most of the milking in the early morning, Father could still be found in the cow-byre when we wandered out with the milk pails. Again, his routine never varied: he would release the horses from their stalls into the barnyard, feed the pigs, clean out the manure to the back of the barn, and empty the milk into the separator. All the time, he spoke only if spoken to, and then often in one-or two-word sentences. It was as if even a waste of words was close to a mortal sin during those lean Depression years.

Father's work-load was endless, regardless of the season. In the fall it was the cropping. Long, full days on the binder. Piling the hay into the mow. Fixing the inevitable machinery break-downs that came as regularly as death and the yearly tax bill. Pulling gravel from the pit for the customers along the Northcote road and bartering with them for the payment.

The big, silver pocket-watch, which was fastened to the breast pocket of his overalls with a piece of leather strap, would tell Father when it was dinner time. Then he would eat, lie down on the couch in the kitchen for a quick noonhour nap, and be off again to the fields or the barns. Those few moments of sleep would refresh him, and he would attack the afternoon as if the day were just beginning. But, by the time Father returned to the house for supper, his walk would be slower and his head just a bit more stooped.

Although our father offered no more than the occasional sentence to our conversations around the table, he was wonderfully curious about our day and what we had done and seen at school or on the Northcote road on the way home. But often before we had finished our last mouthful, Father would already be on his way to the couch for a little "catch-eye" as he called it. With his pipe resting on his chest, he let out soft, even snores in spite of the chaos of rattling dishes, evening games, and singsongs around him.

We could almost set our clocks to his evening routine. Once he had a bit of sleep, he would roll off the couch, reach for the *Ottawa Farm Journal*, and move to the rocker. There, with his stockinged feet on the oven door, he would read the entire paper even if it were two or three days old. Rarely did he comment on what he read, but we often saw quick puffs of smoke emitting from his pipe. To us, this was a sign that he didn't like what he was reading.

When it was bedtime, winter or summer, Father would make a final trip to the barns to tend the livestock. This was Mother's cue to put on a pot of green tea, which he would drink from a large, open cup with two or three slices of bread that had been toasted over the coals in the Findlay Oval. Father would stoke the fire for the night, putting on a big log, then he would go to the downstairs bedroom, frame himself in the doorway, wave to all of us, and tell us not to forget our prayers — which was unnecessary since Mother would never let us put a foot under the quilts until we had prayed for everyone in the County.

Father's day would be over, but it would be repeated the next morning, and the next, and the one after that. He rarely complained of what now seems to us an endless life filled with boredom and repetition. But when Father lamented about his lot in life, it was not for what was past, but for what might have been — had it not been any other time but the thirties.

FATHER LOVED HIS NOON-HOUR NAP. IN THE WINTER HE TOOK HIS NAPS ON THE KITCHEN COUCH; IN THE SUMMER HE COULD BE FOUND NAPPING IN THE BACKYARD — ALWAYS WITH HIS BELOVED PIPE.

The honeymoon suite

It was one of the worst fall nights I can remember. The wind was howling down the stove-pipe and rattling the damper, and the cold, icy sleet was hitting the windows like needles. But inside our old log house it was cozy and warm. More than once Father said, "It's not fit for man or beast outside tonight."

We children were involved in our usual Saturday night games around the kitchen table when we heard a faint tap at the door that grew louder. Father opened it to a rush of rain and sleet, and two bedraggled creatures filled the doorway.

They certainly didn't look as if they belonged outside on a night like this. They were dressed fit to kill. At least they had started out dressed fit to kill, but they stood there soaked to the skin — he in a pin-striped suit with a frozen flower in his lapel and she in a silk dress with once flowing sleeves that were plastered to her arms like flypaper. She had on a wide-brimmed hat with silk flowers, which hung down around her face like wilted lettuce. Her vision out of one eye was completely obliterated, and she had to turn her face sideways to see into the kitchen. We couldn't tell if the water streaming down her face was tears or rain.

In a rush of words the young man said they had just been married in Douglas that evening and were heading into Renfrew for a weekend honeymoon when their borrowed car had given up the ghost at our laneway. They had obviously abandoned the car there and walked toward the lamplight coming from our windows. It was a long walk, and the little, cardboard suitcase they were carrying looked as if it was about to fall apart.

Mother ushered them into the kitchen, and they stood in front of the Findlay Oval. Father offered to drive them into town in our old car, but first they would have to wait until he fixed a couple of flat tires. The old cars in the thirties were notorious for getting flats at the most inopportune times. Taking them in the buggy was out of the question; they would have frozen to death by the time they reached Briscoe's store.

Then Mother suggested they should spend the night at the farm. The young man turned beet red, and I thought the new bride was going to cry again. Emerson, who was quite a bit older than I, started to snicker at I knew not what, and Mother threw him a look that would wither an oak tree.

Mother went into a quick consultation with Audrey, so I knew they were discussing where the newlyweds would sleep. Father poked at the fire, bringing the kettle to the boil to see if he could pour some warmth into their bones with a cup of strong, green tea.

It was finally decided that Mother and Father would move out of their bed downstairs and up into one of the three small rooms we five children shared. Audrey was fetched for clean flannelette sheets and a pair of our best hand-embroidered pillow slips.

The young girl was growing increasingly uncomfortable, which was beyond my comprehension. And all the while my brothers were snickering behind the palms of their hands. Father finally sent them packing upstairs. I could hear them laughing, and I knew without looking up that they were peeking down the stove-pipe hole that went from the kitchen into the upstairs hall.

Mother and Audrey finally had the downstairs bedroom organized. Mother took a blooming geranium off the kitchen cupboard and put it on the little table beside the bed. "Just to give a bit of colour," she said to no one in particular.

The newlyweds were still in their soaking clothes, which Mother suggested they hand out to her when they undressed. She would drape them around the stove in the kitchen so they would dry out overnight. The young bride turned beet red again and said nothing, but the bridegroom said that would be fine.

I was taken upstairs with Audrey and am loathe to confess that we joined the brothers around the stove-pipe hole too. "I bet she doesn't go into the bedroom at all," Emerson said. "She looks like a scared rabbit." This perfectly innocent remark sent Everett rolling on the floor. But we soon saw Mother talking in soothing sounds to the young thing, and finally we saw our parents drape the couple's sopping clothes on the backs of a couple of kitchen chairs close to the stove.

My brothers snickered long into the night, and our parents, who had taken over the back bedroom, hushed them up time and again. Finally, Mother came out in her long, flannelette nightgown and gave them each a sound cuff on the ear that settled them down in a hurry.

Sunday morning broke clear as a bell, and Father got the boys out of bed at the crack of dawn. Audrey and I heard Mother say she wanted them out of the house before the newlyweds emerged from the downstairs bedroom. We could hear Father rhyming off all the chores he wanted them to do in the barns, chores that were rarely done on a Sunday, but he wanted to keep them busy until it was time for church.

When Audrey and I came down, the clothes near the stove were stiff as boards, and Mother was getting ready to iron them. Father had hitched up the buggy and it was waiting at the kitchen door. The young man ate as if the meal was to be his last on earth, but the bride just poked at her bacon and eggs and hung her head as if she had been caught with her hand in the cookie jar.

The young man asked Father to drive them back to the homestead in Douglas instead of into Renfrew; he had to be back in time for the evening chores. He said someone would be around later to try to get the old car going.

They headed out the lane, Father sitting at the outside of the seat and chewing on his pipe, the bride squashed between him and her new husband. She had on the wide hat and the flowers looked just as dead as they did the night before.

Audrey and I waved. From the window in the cow-byre the three brothers were peeking through the glass. And the smiles they wore the night before were still on their faces.

Playing with the Bijous

A rare treat indeed it was when our family went out on a night other than Saturday. So we were quite surprised when Mother announced that we would be going to the pictures at the O'Brien Theatre in Renfrew on a Monday night. We had been ordered to hurry with our chores, and the kitchen got the fastest 'lick and a promise' we had ever witnessed.

Naturally, we were delighted. We dared not question Mother's motives in case she changed her mind — although this seemed rather unlikely since she was as excited as we were.

We made it to the O'Brien in plenty of time; in fact, we were just about the first ones there — other than the Bijous, a group of six local musicians who were already tuning up at the front of the stage. We settled into our seats, thrilled to be so close to the screen. Mother nodded to the musicians, making it known that she was there.

Her actions began to embarrass us, in fact. All the time the musicians played the old favourites like "K K K Katie", Mother kept time to the music by tapping her toes and softly clapping her hands. Each time they finished a number, she beamed as if she had just been treated to a concert by the Philharmonic Orchestra.

In those days the Bijous played every Monday night at the O'Brien Opera House. My mother thought they were the most wonderful musicians in Renfrew County — in the thirties I daresay they were outstanding.

Mother had certainly succeeded in making herself noticed because when it was time to begin the movie, the title of which I no longer remember, each musician in turn bowed to her. Mother's face glowed like an electric light bulb. Then, just as they were about to make their way through the velvet curtains at the side of the stage, she hissed, "You children behave yourselves. I will be right back."

We were well into the picture when Mother re-appeared. It was too dark to see her expression, but she leaned into the front row and said, "All right children, it's time to go." We let out great wails that the show had barely begun, but Mother was having none of our protests. "Come, I said." We left our seats and slowly shuffled up the aisle backwards, wondering what possessed our mother to insist we leave in the middle of a movie. And after good money had been paid to get in!

We lamented all the way home, but Mother gave not one clue as to her odd behaviour. The only thing she did say was, "Never mind, we will be coming back next Monday night." Then she added, "And there is no need to tell your father. He will find out soon enough." We felt we were conspirators to a crime.

Even though we thought it never would, Monday arrived. Imagine going to a movie on a school night: Father was mumbling to himself and chewing his pipe as we all climbed into the old Model T with Mother behind the wheel. She was singing by the time we hit the Northcote road and driving the car flat out. Father clutched his old, straw hat to his head; his eyes never left the road. And we five kids hung on for dear life in the back seat. Mother hadn't even given us enough time to fasten on the side curtains, and the wind blew through us like a tornado.

When we arrived at the theatre, Mother went right up to the manager and whispered a few words to him. With a flourish, he waved us into the theatre; we didn't even have to buy tickets. Right down to the front seat we were marched. The Bijous had already assembled, and they smiled to Mother in greeting. She piled her coat on Audrey's lap, opened her purse, took out her seventy-five-cent harmonica, and headed for the one empty chair in front of the stage. Father's mouth shot open and his pipe fell to the floor. "Good Lord, she's going to play with the Bijous." By this time the theatre was almost full. Mother, who was dressed in a print dress, stood out like a tulip in a cabbage patch; the men in the band wore black tuxedos.

Then the music began. We could hear the high, sweet tones of Mother's harmonica above the saxophone and the banjo. It didn't matter what the musicians played, Mother was right there with them. After each number the audience applauded. First with a little uncertainty and then with more confidence, Mother even stood when the musicians took their bows.

Too soon the stage lights blinked on and off: the movie was about to start. When the men disappeared behind the curtains, Mother came and sat with us for the rest of the show. I couldn't tell you what movie was playing because I spent most of the time looking at my mother's profile in the dim light. I remember marvelling at how clever she was and being proud of her talent.

Our family fully expected tht Mother would be playing with the Bijous every Monday night, but this was not the case. Playing with a band was something she always wanted to do, and once was enough. At the time Father thought the whole thing was pretty silly. But many times after when they attended some of the Saturday night square dances, Mother would be playing the harmonica and Father would often be heard to say, "When Mabel played with the Bijous . . .." It was then we knew he was as proud of her as we were.

THE LIGHT FILTERS THROUGH
THE CHEESECLOTH SCREEN,
AND BRIGHTENS THE CORNER
WHEREIN LIVES MY HEART.
I LOOK AROUND AND CHERISH
WHAT I SEE —
MY HEART, MY KITCHEN,
MY WALLS —
THIS IS MY LIFE.

— MABEL ERNESTINE LAPOINTE

When Mother's heart sang

It was easy to determine Mother's moods when I was a little girl. When she was sad, her eyes would take on a far-away look and her voice would lose the excitement it usually had. When she was annoyed, she had a habit of drumming her fingers on the nearest flat surface. Ah, but when her heart was happy, there was that whistle of hers. Even now, so many years later, I can hear in my mind's ear her whistle . . . .

Mother was almost always happy, and nothing told us more that all was well than the high, sweet whistle in which she indulged. She whistled like a bird — high-pitched, strong, and full of melody — and we often saw her stop in mid-chore, go to the kitchen window, tilt her head up, and whistle as if the entire world was outside listening. Nothing would interfere with her reverie. And it didn't matter where I was in the house, I would have to stop to listen.

Mother also whistled when she was annoyed. But this whistle was distinctly different. It was a low, dull monotone, with no tune I could recognize. This whistle was saved for times when the bread wouldn't rise, or she couldn't get the old Singer sewing machine to do what she wanted. When she combined her two habits, that of drumming her fingers and whistling her low, tuneless sounds, this was our signal to stay clear until she worked out whatever was bothering her.

She always whistled when she was working in the kitchen. She delighted us all by cutting beans or peeling potatoes to the rhythm of her music. I can remember being delighted at hearing those whistles and watching Mother's eyebrows raise with a high note as a bean cutting flew into the pot. And she knew she was delighting me too. So the performance became a ritual.

Mother especially liked to whistle hymns, but from time to time she would stop long enough to switch to the words. And these she belted out with great gusto in a deep alto voice. Her favourite was "The Old Rugged Cross". The ability to combine her singing with her whistling, to me, was a remarkable talent. Mother also could whistle at the same time, which probably seems to most people an utter impossibility. But it was so. I can remember thinking that she was clever enough to be on the stage. And I doubted there was anyone in Renfrew County who possessed such a marvellous ability.

Just as we were taught to bake bread and embroider, we were taught to whistle. Mother would sit us before her on a chair, and we would have to press our hands against her cheeks and get the ***feel*** of the whistle. At first, we would just be blowing out air. What a joy when that first squeaky sound escaped from our pursed lips. Never one to be contented with mediocrity, Mother eventually had us all whistling in perfect harmony, and our nightly singsongs were sprinkled with choruses of whistling. Her most remarkable feat on these occasions was convincing Father to join in because we always said he was born with a deaf ear for music and had absolutely no rhythm whatsoever. Mother insisted he take part. I suspect now that he enjoyed the singsongs as much as the rest of us.

As youngsters, we whistled when we worked in the fields, when we walked to school, and when we went to the back pasture for the cows. These days, I notice that not too many people whistle anymore — at least for no reason at all. And I think this is a great pity because those days in the thirties when whistling was so much a part of our lives were full of joy and contentment.

When I see someone sad or angry or troubled, I always think of Mother, who used to say that it's pretty hard to frown or cry and whistle at the same time.

A quarter's worth at the Renfrew fair

Every year when we travelled from Northcote to the Renfrew fair, we were each given a quarter to spend as we wished. Only a child of the Depression can appreciate what transpired to allow our parents such a free hand with their money at a time when every penny had to have a mission. In order for my three brothers, my sister, and me to be given such a princely sum, my mother would have to make a trip to Renfrew before the fair to sell a few chickens, home-made butter, and anything else that could be translated into cash.

When the five quarters were being doled out, we would line up in a row in the kitchen with our hands outstretched, as if we were receiving a communion wafer. My brothers would thrust their money deep into the pockets of their breeks, while my sister, Audrey, and I would tie our quarters into the corner of one of our school hankies. These we would roll into a tight ball and press into our fists during the drive to Renfrew.

At the fair, my brother Emerson would take off like someone possessed. He always had one mission in mind, and that was to get rid of the quarter as quickly as possible. He headed right for the first stand, where often the prize was something that didn't interest him in the slightest. But Emerson was fair game for the hawkers: we knew that within minutes of entering the fair grounds Emerson and his quarter would soon be parting company.

My other two brothers were only slightly more cautious. Whereas Emerson would spend his money on the first thing that caught his eye, Everett and Earl would take a walk through the midway first. Then they would settle on something like a ride on the swings and an ice cream cone, and just perhaps they would have enough left for some pink candy floss. A quarter bought a lot in the thirties.

It was to be expected that immediately after parting with his money Emerson would have regrets. This was because he usually had nothing to show for it. He would have tried — unsuccessfully — to outwit the hawker who was guessing ages and weight. And he would have learned that firing the rifle in a canvas booth was different from trying to knock a tin can off a fence post with the '22 back on the farm.

Once his money was gone, Emerson had little else to do but wander into the livestock barns and spend the rest of the day watching the judging. He vowed he got great enjoyment out of that part of the fair, but Audrey was doubtful. She reminded me that he was always expressing his distaste for the cows, sheep, and pigs on the farm and that he constantly said how he couldn't wait to get off the farm when he grew up.

Emerson would try, with a little luck, to talk my two other brothers into making him a small loan. This was laughable, as he had absolutely no hope of ever paying back the money, a fact that didn't escape Everett and Earl.

Audrey and I handled our fair money differently. Still with the quarters tied tightly in our hankies and scrunched in our hands, we would walk the entire fair from the front gate to the livestock barns. No hawker was able to entice us: as they vied for our money, we would walk by them with our noses in the air, showing just a corner of our hankies to let them know we could spend a few pennies if we had a mind to. We would walk around for about an hour. Like leaving the icing on the cake to the last mouthful, we wanted to savour the delicious excitement of having that much money in our possession until the very last moment.

Audrey invariably spent her quarter on the rides. She loved the ferris wheel, which scared the starch right out of me. So I would stand beside the big machine and watch it take my sister higher and higher and finally to the very top, where the chair teetered precariously. The truth of the matter is, the only ride I liked was the merry-go-round, but Emerson had convinced me that anyone seven years of age was much too old for that nonsense.

Long after Audrey had spent her quarter, I would still be clutching mine in a cramped, sweaty fist, waiting for an elusive something that I hoped would come along.

In our family there was no such thing as buying hot dogs or chocolate milk at the Renfrew fair. Mother would have packed a lunch so that we wouldn't have to spend our money on something as frivolous as fair refreshments. We'd make our way back to the car, where Mother would spread out a white sheet on the grass and pass around big, farm-style sandwiches and cold milk in a thermos. Slabs of cake and huge oatmeal cookies were always on hand. But before we could eat or even put our hands on the food, Mother would pass around a wet, soapy face-cloth to make sure that the germs we had picked up from walking around the fair grounds would not be transferred to our mouths.

In the afternoon Audrey and I would wander into the hall to take a look once again at the embroidery work and the baking. By this time, Audrey had been relieved of her money; I still clutched the quarter in my hand. She would wonder, in a sharp voice, if I ***ever*** intended to part with it — but she knew the answer as well as I.

When it was time to wander back to the car — we had to be home for the evening chores — the twenty-five cent piece would still be firmly tied in my hanky. I don't really know why I hung onto the quarter. Perhaps I felt it would be a long time before I had such a sum of money in my possession again. Or perhaps I thoroughly enjoyed feeling smug when we crawled into the car and I could finally untie the hanky and fondle the money in front of everyone, content in the knowledge there was a great deal of truth to Father's favourite phrase that "a fool and his money are soon parted."

THIS AD APPEARED IN THE *RENFREW MERCURY* IN 1933. (*COURTESY OF MARJORIE LINDSAY.*)

The Saturday night bath

I don't know how old I was when I first became aware of my body. Perhaps six or seven. Inhibitions over nudity I didn't have — until that one night my older and much wiser sister pointed out to me that there was a vast difference between boys and girls.

Until then I was content to have my Saturday night bath in front of the old Findlay Oval where shafts of delicious heat reached out and touched my naked body. I delighted in running through the house like a young antelope without being encumbered by clothes whenever I got the chance — usually between skinning off my long drawers and crawling into a warm, homemade, flannelette nightgown.

But all of that freedom from self-consciousness came to an abrupt end one Saturday night when Audrey, given the task of making sure I had washed behind my ears and scrubbed my knees and elbows, related to me the tragedies that could hit me like a sledgehammer if I didn't cover up.

Our kitchen was large, with the work area at one end and the big pine table with benches on either side at the other. Audrey and I were in front of the stove, I immersed in a wash-tub of warm, soapy water and Audrey on her knees beside me. Sitting around the table, my three brothers were engrossed in a favourite Saturday night card game and Mother was at one end trying to keep order. Father, as usual, was dozing in the old rocker with his feet on the seat of a chair and the *Ottawa Farm Journal* lying across his chest like a blanket.

I loved my Saturday night bath, which was always taken before anyone else in the family. It was a time when I had my beloved sister to myself, when she would, if she was in the right mood, tell me marvellous, little tidbits of information that inflamed my already fertile mind.

On this particular Saturday night, Audrey had lamented that she thought it was time I took on the task of bathing myself.

She wanted to play cards, and she said she didn't think it was fair that every Saturday night she had to spend some of the evening on her hands and knees with her hands in the laundry tub. Her lament fell on deaf ears.

So she came to the task with a sour face, and it looked very much as if we weren't going to enjoy the usual chatty exchange I looked forward to every week. Stark naked, I had run from the upstairs bedroom where I had shed my clothes, past the gang at the table who hadn't raised as much as an eye in my direction, and had jumped into the big, copper tub with gusto.

It was then Audrey, with a scowl on her usually placid face, whispered to me that I should put an end to appearing uncovered in front of everyone. I asked her why, with all the innocence of a child who had never before given much thought to the subject. "Because," she said, with a knowing look on her face, "I have known people who were struck dead in their tracks." I wondered immediately which person was struck dead, the one who was naked or the beholder. "The person who is exposing himself, of course," Audrey replied with a cross look. I looked down at my bony chest that showed not a ripple, except for the rows of ribs that encircled me, and I tried to visualize what was so terrible about that part of my anatomy. I immediately asked who would be responsible for my demise if such a thing did occur. "The devil?" I asked. "Of course not," Audrey hissed. "God, that's who." I mulled over in my mind this latest bit of terrifying information, and I couldn't imagine how a just God would be remotely interested in me showing my body in front of my family. But Audrey was deadly serious, and I respected and believed every word she said.

I begged her to get a kitchen chair and place it in front of the wash-tub, and then drape the couch quilt around it so I could protect myself from the looks that would be sure to send me to the land of my forefathers. Audrey complied. Soon I was completely hidden from view, and I continued my bath in relative confidence that I was saved from a sudden and terrible end.

But the Saturday night bath was never quite the same. From then on I draped the area with a blanket and undressed behind it; I put on my nightgown in the same fashion. And I never again ran through the house naked. I became very conscious of my body and took to undressing in the dark. Neither did I ever question Audrey about the matter. After all, she was much older and, I thought, very wise. And I was much too in awe of God to put Him to the test as well.

The Hallowe'en caper

Hallowe'en in the thirties was a time for great frivolity as a rule. But I can remember one year in particular when the evening turned into a disaster.

Our mother had given us permission to have a party. Back then this meant that everyone in the community including parents, grandparents, and children of all ages was invited. Fortunately, not everyone showed up. But a goodly number always came to the old country parties, and I can remember the fun and laughter and how the young mingled with the old.

My cousin Ronny and his brother were with us this particular Hallowe'en, as luck would have it. Otherwise, the whole evening might have passed like so many other Hallowe'ens — in simple fun and laughter, with plenty of good, country food and old-time music.

Everyone arrived in costume. Naturally we five children and the Montreal cousins were dressed for the occasion as well. Not much imagination had been used with our costumes, I'm afraid. We rubbed our faces with stove black and wore oversized combination underwear stuffed with pillows or our father's overalls, and then we went through the exaggerated exercise of pretending to guess the identity of one another. Long, red ringlets were pretty difficult to conceal, and Cecil's ears, which stuck out from the sides of his head like grape leaves. Nonetheless, the act of pretending that everyone's identity was a mystery seemed to add to the excitement.

By eight o'clock the old log house was fairly jumping. The kitchen had been cleared for dancing, and the parlour had been stripped of unnecessary furniture. Instead of oil lamps, we had carved pumpkins with home-made wax candles glowing inside. The older children had arranged all sorts of games, with many involving mysterious trips to the outside privy, which for some reason added to the whole mystery of the evening.

By ten o'clock the littlest children had dozed off on the kitchen couch and some had been carried upstairs to the beds. But Ronny, it seemed to me, was just getting into high gear. He was only about eight, but sleep was the farthest thing from his mind as he stood off to one side of the parlour with that air about him that I had learned to recognize as a look of sheer mischief. I could feel my stomach go into knots because, as sure as lightning, he was planning something.

I wandered over to where he was standing and said through clenched teeth, "What are you up to Ronny?" "What makes you think I'm up to anything. I'm just standing here looking at the people and thinking how quiet everyone is. I think they need something to liven them up," he said. "Don't you dare try anything, Ronny. This has been a nice party and if you spoil it now I'll kill you." I tried to sound severe and attempted to give off an air of authority that I didn't feel.

By this time people had settled down into every available chair around the room to await the lunch, which had arrived in baskets and shoeboxes with each guest. They were chatting easily, as country folk do, contented with the evening and happy to be among friends. I saw Ronny sneak upstairs, and I felt a wave of relief having thought he perhaps had decided to go to bed. But within minutes he was back downstairs carrying a white shoebox under his arm. I never took my eyes off him.

He moved over to the pump organ, which sat kitty-corner in the parlour. I saw him crouch down on his haunches close to the wall where no one could see him. He lowered the shoebox slowly to the floor. I stood spell-bound, terrified of what was coming next. Then he lifted the lid and tilted the box. About six, grey field mice flew out of the opening and tore across the parlour floor in every direction. It took less than a split second for the first one to be spotted: Mrs. Duffy, who sang in the choir and who Ronny said had a voice like a mooing cow, let out a scream and leaped right up on top of a fellow's knee, who was sitting with his chair tilted back against the wall. They both went down like a ton of bricks. The mice were frantically trying to find an opening through which to escape. But with people lining the parlour walls there was little place for them to go. By this time the entire room was a shambles, and the people in the kitchen crowded in the parlour doorway to see the show. I looked over and saw that Ronny had a look of absolute bliss on his face. I saw him toss the tell-tale shoebox behind the organ.

By some miracle the mice all found avenues of escape — but not before every woman and young girl in the room had gone into hysterics. Some of them had dropped their tea cups full of hot tea; others were already heading for the coat rack before the dust had settled. My mother was making apologies and saying she couldn't imagine where the mice had come from, which was quite true because I was obviously the only one who had witnessed Ronny's little caper.

In less time than it took to shake a stick, the house was cleared. Audrey was in tears, but the brothers thought the whole thing was pretty funny. Then I saw Ronny coming down the stairs in his flannelette pyjamas, faking a yawn and rubbing his eyes. "What happened, Aunty?" he was saying. "I was sound asleep, and I heard this awful commotion."

I couldn't believe what I was hearing. Ronny looked me square in the eye, knowing full well I was well aware who had caused the commotion. But he also knew full well that I would be the last one to tell on him because, as well as loving him like one of my own brothers, I also admired him. Back then Ronny was one of the few people I knew who could break every rule in the book and get away with it, who could dream up more mischief than enough, and who showed more spunk than anyone else I knew. No, his secret was safe with me.

Long ringlets no more

Not unlike an April rain storm, Aunt Lizzie blew in from Regina to our old log house ready to take command and change the course of our lives. My father's sister, although generous and benevolent, nonetheless intimidated my mother by ceaselessly pointing out all her failings as a farmer's wife. She filled us five children with awe and apprehension.

Aunt Lizzie's first target was my long, red ringlets. In this day and age, she told my mother through clenched teeth, simply no one wore yard-long ringlets. After all, she said, this was the nineteen-thirties and all city people, regardless of age, were sporting bobbed hair.

My mother dealt with this pronouncement in her usual calm way. With an air of authority, she made it known that she preferred my long, red ringlets to bobbed hair, while conceding that Aunt Lizzie's marcelled short cut was very smart. Aunt Lizzie railed about the foolishness of tying her hair up in rags to make the ringlets and the agony she was sure I suffered with each and every comb-out. My head went back and forth like someone watching a tennis match, as I wondered who would win this bout.

Secretly I hoped it would be Aunt Lizzie. Cecil, the horrible boy whose desk was right behind mine at school, had dunked my ringlets into the ink-well more than once. On another occasion, he had tied them together with binder twine and anchored the knot to the top of his desk. I almost broke my neck when I stood up, and the desk clattered like a broken rain-barrel. I was tricked and surprised by both these pranks because he carried them out with a deft hand on an unsuspecting victim.

It wouldn't have distressed me in the least if I was rid of the long, red ringlets. But Mother changed the subject; as far as she was concerned the issue was over.

When Aunt Lizzie was visiting the farm, it was always a special treat for me to accompany her to town. Mother always elected to stay home. I suspect she was glad to take advantage of a few hours of peace and quiet. When Saturday rolled round Aunt Lizzie and Father headed into town with me nestled between them in the buggy knowing that we would come back with such things as bologna and oranges. The first pair of white stockings I ever owned in my life had come my way on one such excursion.

Father dropped us off on the main street before he headed off to do his weekly business at the grist mill and hardware store. Aunt Lizzie had a firm hold of my hand as we crossed the street heading straight for Ducharme's beauty salon. I had no idea what she was planning to do — it dimly crossed my mind that she was going to have a wave perhaps. So it came as a great surprise when she pointed to my head and said, "Cut it."

I never argued with an elder. Such was our upbringing that we often said that if an adult pushed us head first into the Bonnechere River, we'd smile all the way down to the bottom. I said nothing when the woman in the shop placed a short board across the arms of the chair and helped me climb up. "Are you sure?" she asked; she was more apprehensive than I. "Of course I'm sure," Aunt Lizzie said in her most domineering voice. "Why do you think we're here? And you might as well give her a bit of a permanent wave while you're at it." Right away I felt a twinge of excitement since Marguerite — that paragon of virtue and my worst enemy at school — had a permanent, which was the envy of every girl in Admaston Township. Now I was to have a head of beautiful, short curls too!

The hairdresser cut off the ringlets one by one and laid them out on a table. They looked like long, red sausages. After what seemed like hours, having survived nearly choking to death on the permanent solution, my face was beet red from the ordeal. I looked at myself in the mirror and I could barely recognize the girl who looked back at me. A mass of red fuzz encircled my head and stood out about six inches all round. Aunt Lizzie crowed like a rooster and proceeded to peel off a couple of bills from a roll that was as thick as a newspaper.

When we came outside I could see Father standing beside the buggy in front of Thacker's garage. I ran across the street as if my feet had wings. He stared right by me — only when I tugged at his sleeve did he know who it was. His pipe started to bob up and down in his mouth, and I thought he was going to start chewing on the reins. Father's only comment to his sister was: "Wait until Mabel sees what you've gone and done, Lizzie. She's goin' to be some mad."

Well, to say Mother was "some mad" would be the understatement of the decade. First she slammed me against her chest and murmured, "My baby," at which point Aunt Lizzie wisely decided to go upstairs and change her dress. Everyone was in the kitchen. I will always be grateful to Audrey for saying, "I think it's beautiful." My three brothers were rolling on the floor with laughter. Emerson said I looked like the old, bearskin horse blanket dyed red. Earl said I smelled to high heaven, and Everett, who was the oldest and should have known better, said he bet my hair would fall out before the weekend was over. The top of my head was wet where my mother's tears had landed. She kept moaning and saying to Father that "it had taken seven years to grow that hair and in one day that sister of yours has ruined it." By the time Aunt Lizzie came down, Mother was all cried out. Mother declared that the damage was done and that we could do nothing about it now. We will just have to wait until the hair grows back in.

For the rest of Aunt Lizzie's stay Mother was civil, but that was about all. Every morning, when I was going through the ordeal of having those tight curls combed, Mother would take a little, wooden ruler and measure the hair at the back of my neck. It took ages for the wave to grow out. Never again was I to have my long ringlets hanging down my back to my waist.

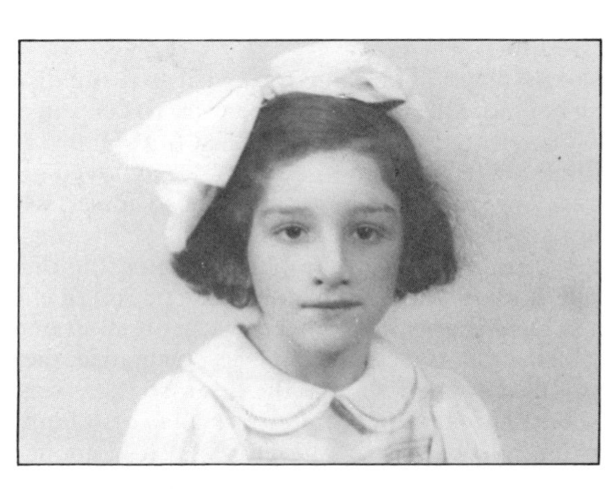

THIS IS WHAT MY HAIR LOOKED LIKE AFTER AUNT LIZZIE WAS FINISHED WITH IT.

A chocolate bar mistake

One day, back in the thirties, we five children missed the first day of school. Just the day before, Aunt Lizzie had left our farm after a prolonged visit. Father had driven her to the CPR station right after church for her long trip back to Regina. As Mother had lamented that her visit had left little time to tidy the house and get us ready for school, none of us was allowed to go with Father for the drive into Renfrew. We all dearly loved the trip to the station as it gave us a chance to see the trains.

Mother had better things for us to do. The bedroom Aunt Lizzie had used had to be torn apart. The mattresses of feathers had to be turned, the mats beaten with the broom on the back fence, and the wooden floor scrubbed. Since Aunt Lizzie had been with us most of the month of August, my sister, Audrey, and I had turned over the little washstand we shared. It, too, had to be wiped out before we could put back our few possessions. The work was akin to a fall house-cleaning and every one of us had been pressed into service.

Aunt Lizzie never once came for a visit that she didn't leave something behind. She always said we were to keep anything we found, and this suited Audrey and me just fine. One year she left a pair of high-heeled red shoes, which I dearly loved playing in; another year a box of face powder and a laced corset, which until her dying day she denied was hers.

On this particular day Audrey had emptied the one drawer in the washstand. It was here she found the packet of chocolates, wrapped in silver paper. The packet was still all in one flat bar and contained about twelve, small pieces. Of course, the brothers had also spotted it when it fell to the floor, so there was nothing else to do but share it with them. Audrey had also found a long, pearl hat-pin, but we weren't nearly as excited about this find as we were about the chocolate bar. It didn't take us long to gobble it down after Audrey had divided it evenly into five pieces.

By late afternoon the room was shining like a door knob. As always, Mother was on her inspection tour to make sure we had done everything she had ordered and that it was done to her liking. It was then the pains hit. I was the first to notice. It was as if someone had taken a handful of my stomach and was slowly but fiercely kneeding it into a knot. I barely made it to the outside privy. After the great feeling of relief from sitting on the two-holer, I heard Audrey thundering down the path, announcing that she was coming in. She was doubled over with pains. Even though Mother had always insisted a visit to the privy was a very private matter, I could see Audrey would be sharing the experience with me this time. I was just about to leave when two of my brothers roared from the summer house door that they needed to get in and to hurry up or we would live to regret it. Audrey and I exchanged places with them, and we could hear great groans of relief coming from inside as we headed back to the house.

We told Mother we ached from head to toe. After she determined, by holding a cool palm to our foreheads that we had no fever, she said we probably ate too much lunch. Audrey and I fell into the nearest chairs, still clutching our bellies. We then saw our youngest brother tear past the kitchen window on his way to the privy, but Emerson and Everett, who were occupying the two seats, wouldn't let him in. He headed for the back of the silo, already undoing the buttons on his breeks.

By then Mother had become suspicious and accused all of us of either eating the small crab-apples by the mail-box or getting into Father's home-made grape wine in the cellar. We assured her that neither was the case. We told her all we had was a small chocolate bar Aunt Lizzie had left in the washstand. Audrey, who still had the wrapper in her pinny pocket, handed it all scrunched up to Mother. "You have just eaten your way through an entire box of laxative," Mother said without emotion. We had never heard of a laxative done up like a chocolate bar. Once or twice a year Mother mixed up a concoction of molasses and soda, which we considered more a treat than a treatment, and we took it whether we needed it or not.

Too sick to eat supper, none of us moved a fraction from the summer kitchen door. Finally, Mother had to lay down a rule that Audrey and I would use the privy and the boys would have to go behind the silo.

The trips went on all night, rendering us into weak and tired dishrags by morning. We didn't go as frequently, but we went with the same urgency and agony. By eight o'clock in the morning Mother had determined that we couldn't take a chance on going to school, even if it was the first day.

We laid around the house all day. The cramps finally gave way to a feeling of utter and complete exhaustion. We became so nonchalant about going to the privy that eventually we didn't even bother closing the door. Mother said some good always came out of every situation. We couldn't for the life of us see what good emanated from the overdose of laxative. But she said we had been spared from the fall clean-out of molasses and soda. However, we considered this more of a punishment than a reward.

I THOUGHT AUNT LIZZIE DRESSED IN THE HEIGHT OF FASHION. SHE WORE LOVELY, BIG RINGS AND MATCHING HATS AND PURSES. TO ME, SHE WAS ALWAYS ELEGANT.

The dastardly deed

Other than me, I guess my brother Earl was the most timid of us all. He was fine-featured and small for his age, and when my giant of a brother Emerson wanted to antagonize him, he would call him Evelyn. The closest Earl ever came to losing his temper was to kick a tin can or stick out his tongue. It just wasn't in his nature to cause a commotion.

The same could be said for his integrity. While it was quite easy to associate Emerson with a shady deal, it was unthinkable to picture Earl doing anything that wasn't honourable and open. And that's why, one day back in the thirties, my faith in Earl was shattered when he was caught red-handed committing an act that was completely out of character.

It was a warm fall, I recall. As was common in old log homes, the windows were perfect resting places for the thousands of house flies trying to seek shelter from the occasional cold fall day. They came in through the cracks that no amount of stuffing with flour bags could fill, they worked their way up through the space between the pane and the window ledge, and they came in through the doors that never fit tightly enough.

For as long as I can remember, Mother ran a continual war against house flies. She hated them with a passion, claiming they carried more germs than a shovelful of mud. When the flies were at their worst, every child was pressed into service with homemade fly swatters and rolled *Renfrew Mercurys*. But, try as she would, Mother could never keep up with the hundreds of flies that sought refuge in our old log house.

One year, when she realized she was losing the battle, Mother came up with an ingenious idea that worked very well but changed my brother Earl from an honest, upright boy into what we children considered a cunning, tricky delinquent.

Since we were unable to keep up with the fly population, Mother thought she would offer us an incentive to stimulate our efforts. For every twenty-five dead flies we could produce, we would be paid one cent. It didn't take long for us to figure out that in no time we would be millionaires — by the standards of a youngster living in the thirties. So we tackled the job with a vengeance. As we weren't nearly as fussy about handling the flies as Mother, each time we felled one we would rush over to her for an accounting, whereupon she would put another stroke on a piece of paper. At the end of the day we would tally up our score. Among us there was not one who didn't mentally envision the spending spree we were going to go on when we hit Renfrew the very next Saturday night.

But then we noticed that, for several days running, Earl had four times as many strokes on the paper than the rest of us. Mother, who assured us that only she was making the markings, said Earl was simply doing a better job. By Saturday night Earl had earned several pennies, while the rest of us were quickly coming to the conclusion that the exercise was hardly worth our efforts.

By a stroke of luck, Audrey and I discovered why Earl was able to produce more dead flies. One time, just after he had made an accounting, as always he had been sent outside by Mother to dispose of the bodies. Audrey and I were in the drive-shed — the purpose escapes me now. We saw Earl come in silently, looking around to make sure he wasn't being followed. Audrey and I hid in the shadows since Earl's suspicious movements led us to believe that all was "not above the water."

Earl went to Father's workbench and, crouching beside it, removed a glass jar from the dark depths at the back. Audrey and I were peeking over the mass of nail barrels and other pieces of machinery and trappings that filled the drive-sheds of the day. We saw Earl carefully unscrew the lid and dump a handful of dead flies into the jar, which was almost full to the brim with their dead comrades. It was then we knew how Earl was fast becoming rich. He was simply recycling the flies.

Just as silently as he had entered, Earl left the drive-shed. And we had a decision to make: should we tell Mother, or confront Earl. We decided on the latter since Mother had little patience for tattletales.

Earl was devastated to learn that we had cottoned on to his scheme. He beat us to the house, reasoning that the truth had better come from his mouth than ours. Mother, of course, showed the usual concern when she thought one of her children had conducted a dishonest act, but she was more than mollified when she saw the jar full of dead flies. She decided Earl could keep his earnings, and she said she was sure he would never perform in such a fashion again. However, the rest of us were furious that Earl was not punished severely. And we were even more furious because he had taken on a pious look that we thought was not befitting a criminal.

Mother simply beamed at Earl on Sunday morning: he had come downstairs ready for church, with his hair slicked down and his face shining and looking like a choirboy, and announced that his entire earnings from killing the flies were being turned over to his Sunday school teacher to help feed the Armenian orphans. We had no idea if there were any orphans in Armenia, but Earl had read about their plight at one time or another in the *Family Herald* or *Weekly Star*. He had completely redeemed himself in Mother's eyes. And the rest of us wondered for a long time if crime, in fact, did pay.

OF THE THREE BOYS, EMERSON, EVERETT, AND EARL (LEFT TO RIGHT), EARL WAS THE YOUNGEST AND THE QUIETEST. SO, WHEN HE COMMITTED A MISDEMEANOUR IT WAS CONSIDERED A CATASTROPHY.

The collection of stones

Back in the thirties, most children I knew had hobbies — certainly those in our family. My brother Earl carved; Audrey, my older sister, had mounds of scrap-books into which she put every word ever written about the two little princesses, Elizabeth and Margaret Rose. And my best friend, Velma, saved paper dolls. I collected stones.

Stones, especially oval ones and ones with smooth, glistening surfaces, fascinated me. They were everywhere, although my favourites were always to be found on the shores of the Bonnechere River that ran through our property.

These particular stones were well worn and smooth and showed the wear of time. When I took them from the water, they would turn pure white, so I used to call them my magic stones. As was my usual custom, I walked with my eyes focussed on the ground so that I wouldn't miss the perfect stone for my collection. My brother Emerson used to say I would develop a permanent crick in my neck from walking constantly with my head tilted to the ground. I didn't believe him for a minute. I thought he was just jealous as most of his hobbies had gone down to glorious defeat. This was because he would barely get started when he would lose interest and go on to something else.

My father believed that collecting stones wasn't very productive. He often said the countryside was full of rocks just waiting for some fool to pick them up. But, by the same token, he often came home with a new stone for my collection, having found one while he was plowing or walking the back fields. He'd wash it off in the rain barrel, and it would be sitting by my plate at supper time.

I kept my stones on a ledge that ran all around the wall of the bedroom that I shared with Audrey. On the ledge, which separated the sloping ceilings from the walls, I arranged the stones by their different colours. Then I would spend hours re-arranging them, all the time recalling where they had been found.

Some of my stones, I imagined, had real gold imbedded in their surfaces. And I would defy anyone to touch them as I was convinced they were very valuable. It was a constant worry to me that someone would make off with these stones that I considered were worth a goodly sum of money.

One day I came home from school and went upstairs to change into work clothes, as was my habit when I lived on our farm. As soon as I entered the room, I noticed that most of my precious stones were gone. I flew down the stairs, hysterically crying that someone had stolen my collection. I accused Emerson, knowing he was perfectly capable of such a dastardly deed. But he denied it emphatically and pointed an accusing finger at my cousin Ronny, who had stayed on after September to go to school with us in Northcote. As Ronny was known to tell lies on more than one occasion, I didn't believe him when he said he hated stones and that the last thing he was interested in was my stupid collection.

I tore outside to speak to Father, who was bringing in the cows for the evening milking. On my way I passed Mother at the hen house, who vowed she couldn't imagine what had happened to them. Then I came to the pump in the backyard where, stretched out on his belly, was Ronny's young brother, Terry. He had his face pressed against the boards of the pump platform, and beside him was Mother's egg basket and what remained of my precious collection of stones. As Terry didn't hear me come up behind him, he continued right on with what he was doing, dropping one stone at a time between the old boards and listening to them plop in the well, deep in its cavity. I screamed at him and could hardly believe my eyes when he looked up at me with such an innocent face. I ran for Mother, who took the basket from the little boy and handed me what was less than half a dozen stones remaining.

Terry couldn't understand why I was in tears as he was only three at the time. When Mother asked him why he did it, he simply said that the rest of us dropped stones down in the well all the time and that he liked the sound of them dropping.

There was no use lamenting. The stones were gone forever. And I couldn't be angry for long at the little boy with the golden curls and the big, brown eyes, especially when Mother emphasized that he really didn't know he was doing anything wrong.

A long time transpired until my collection was back to its original state before Terry had disposed of most of it. But when we left the farm, I took my precious collection down to the

Bonnechere River and placed the stones along the bank where the water would wash over them and protect them and keep them for all eternity. I would guess they are still there.

ANGELIC TERRY AND HIS OFTEN-TIMES NOT SO ANGELIC BROTHER, RONNY, MY BELOVED YOUNG COUSINS FROM MONTREAL.

A dog named Sport

On looking back now, I see that our family enjoyed more happy times than sad times. We knew there was a Depression, but we five children gave little thought to it. We let our parents carry the burden of wondering from where the next dollar was coming and whether or not the farm would carry on from year to year.

But some sad memories of those days during the thirties on the Renfrew County farm I do have. Although their importance has lessened, they nonetheless remain a part of the mosaic of pictures I carry with me always.

One such memory is of the old farm dog we had when I was a little girl. He was a collie — not a pure-bred — one of hundreds just like him on almost every farm in the community in which we lived. Although it seemed to me he had always been around, in fact he was older than I. Our collie had a thick coat that was mostly white, and in the winter this coat protected him from the frosty Renfrew County winters just as well as if a blanket were wrapped around him.

When he was younger, our collie slept in the house, preferring to roll himself in a ball just inside the back door of the summer kitchen, which offered him some relief from the blowing snow but still let in the fresh, cold air that he so loved.

But age changed many of his earlier habits. Often after supper a soft whining could be heard at the back door, and we knew Sport was telling us that, just for this night, he wouldn't mind moving in so he could be closer to the fire. Mother, who thought all farm animals belonged in the barn, put up no resistance. She even took to folding an old patchwork quilt and placing it beside the cook-stove so Sport would have something on which to lay his poor, old bones.

Sport began to age gradually. First, we noticed that we had to persuade him to fetch the cows at night. When he did rise from his spot at the back door, it was with slow, deliberate movements.

Eventually, through either choice or inability, he would walk to the back of the field with his nose close to the ground and with his usual jaunty tail sweeping the snow. Finally, Sport began to pass up his meals. Even his favourite salt pork rinds would stay untouched in a small heap at the back door until he felt he was in the mood to eat them.

Then one day he started to limp, and before long he was dragging his leg. I warmed milk for him. I passed him pieces of meat from my plate. But nothing seemed to interest him. It was as if he was saying to me, "I'm too tired to be bothered with anything but sleep."

I don't ever recall our having to phone the vet for as long as we lived on the farm. Father tended to the livestock as best he could: if they died, they died. There was no fanfare and little comment. So, naturally, no thought was ever given to taking poor Sport to the vet to see what was ailing him. I asked my father if he thought Sport was hurting. Father said he supposed he was. I wondered if we could give him some of our cod liver oil; Father doubted it would do any good. We could see our beloved, old friend fading before our eyes.

Although Father was often gruff with us and gave little credence to displays of affection, he was compassionate to his children and the farm animals. He couldn't bear to see either suffer. Instinctively, I knew he was labouring with a decision on what to do about Sport. And I remember as if it was yesterday when he finally decided our old friend was to suffer no more.

Father took the gun out from behind the bedroom door, and we saw him take a cartridge from the cupboard and put it in his pocket. We sat frozen in the kitchen as he enticed the dog off the mat. It seemed as if the poor animal was anticipating what lay in store: moving faster than we had seen him move in weeks, Sport waited for the back door to open and, with hardly a sign of a limp, ran outside before Father into the cold, winter's day.

All we heard Mother say was, "Go far from the house."

Father was gone a long time. When he finally came back, he was alone. As children we were spared the details. No one asked about the trip back into the bush and Sport's name was never mentioned again. Although we all ached for the friend that was part of our family for so many years, it was as if he had never been. Eventually another collie came to take his place — that's the way things were done back in those days. The rule for survival was to get on with living and not to fret with what had gone on before.

Hauling water from the pump

Winter was a happy time for us when we lived on the farm back in the thirties. Although the winters, I remember, had much more snow and were colder than they are now, we had wonderful times skating on the Bonnechere and sliding down the back hill on cardboard boxes and old, rusted fenders from an abandoned car.

But some things about winter sent chills up our backs. Even now, thinking of them causes me to shiver, and I rejoice in my two, shiny, chrome taps at the kitchen sink.

Every drop of water we used in the house, from the Saturday night baths to the Monday wash water, had to be carried from the old, green pump that stood like a sentry in our back yard. At the first of the cold season, the task did not carry too much peril, but by the middle of December, it was a life-threatening job to bring water into the house. By this time, the pump platform was a solid, six-inch-thick bed of ice caused from spilled water that had built up over many trips.

We skittered and slipped to the pump with the empty pail, and once we had unhooked the pump from the spout when the pail was full, too often we lost our balance. Unless we were extremely nimble of foot, the ice-cold water from the well cascaded down our legs and ran like rivers inside our gumboots. Then we would have to go through the whole process again of hanging the pail, pumping for ages to get the water back up to the top of the well, and trying to get the pail off the spout and our feet off the bed of ice without a mishap.

The few times we managed this extraordinary feat we rarely made it to the kitchen door unscathed. This was because the pail was heavy and our gumrubbers slipped on the icy, well-beaten path. We had a hard time keeping our balance and the pail banged against our legs, sending freezing water into our boots. Because the job was so distasteful to all of us, our mother made a list of names, which she pinned to the back door.

From then on, one of us was in charge of hauling water for a week. It wasn't uncommon for those of us who remained to gather at the kitchen window, howl with laughter, and bang on the pane when the poor, unfortunate water carrier lost his balance on the pump platform and went down like a ton of bricks with the water pail landing on top of him. It also wasn't uncommon for our hand-knit, woollen mitts to freeze solidly to the wire handle of the pail, where they would stay until the heat of the Findlay Oval unstuck them.

We didn't get away with hauling one pail. Our mother insisted on us hauling three pails of water into the kitchen each time. The big pails were used to fill the reservoir, and on Monday night, after Mother had washed all day, it sometimes took four or five trips to the pump before the big cavity at the back of the stove was filled to Mother's liking.

As well, we had to bring in a smaller, white porcelain pail, which contained our drinking water. It was also used to make tea and boil vegetables. Mother was extremely fussy about this pail of water: it had to sit on a wash-stand near the back window so that it could be kept as cold as possible. Once we set the pail down carefully on the wash-stand, we carefully covered it with a folded, spanking clean, flour-bag tea towel. A white dipper lay in a saucer beside it.

The third pail, which was placed on the bench near the back door, held what Father called our wash-up water. It was used for washing our hands before we laid a hand on a piece of food — and heaven forbid that we should ever touch the dog or a cat and not wash our hands immediately afterwards. In this respect, our mother was serious about cleanliness. Yet she did not insist that this pail be covered.

A big, white dipper floated on the water, and you knew as soon as the dipper started scraping on the bottom of the pail that it was time to make another trek to the pump. Without fail, when one of us dipped into the wash-up pail and transferred the water to the wash-basin, the person who had water duty could be heard hissing, "Go easy on the water." Often we tried, without much success, to trade off water duty with a brother or sister. My brother Emerson would offer his dish of preserved plums to anyone who would take over his pump duties, but there were few takers.

It was many years of battling the outside pump before our father consented to dig a well. When that glorious day arrived, it was as if a whole new world had opened up to us. We were one of the last families in the Northcote area to have water magically pumped into the kitchen. Right up until the last, after Father had finally succumbed to Mother's and our protests, he expressed dissatisfaction with the whole affair. As far as Father was concerned, the whole country was going to hell in a basket. Who ever heard of two wells? Imagine the waste? One pump a spit away from the back door, and another in the kitchen. But to us, who had to battle the winter elements and haul water by the bucketful into the house, the new well was one of the most wonderfully progressive moves we ever made. It was superseded only by another marvellous event — the installation of our first telephone.

AUDREY, ME, EARL, EMERSON, AND EVERETT WITH PETS OUTSIDE THE KITCHEN WINDOW, MOTHER'S FAVOURITE BACKGROUND FOR PICTURE-TAKING.

Aunt Lizzie's false teeth

Aunt Lizzie, my father's sister from Regina, always fascinated me. On her twice-annual visits to our Renfrew County farm during the thirties, her presence never failed to awe me, not only because she turned our house upside down, but because she had about her a glamorous air that I rarely had the opportunity to view at close range.

She stood out on the streets of Renfrew like a rose among the sunflowers. Naturally, her wardrobe couldn't be compared with my mother's who, as most farmwives of the Depression years, rarely had a new dress, let alone all the fancy trappings that went with it.

Aunt Lizzie loved red. She always wore rows on rows of red beads regardless of what costume she happened to have on at the time. My sister, Audrey, and I considered these beads to be at the height of high fashion.

But my one brother Emerson never much cared for Aunt Lizzie. She gave far too many orders and disrupted the routine of the house far too much for his liking. What's more, he often said that under all the paint she wore was a hard and phony face. I, on the other hand, was so intrigued by her that I could find no fault and believed her to be one of the most exciting visitors ever to come to our farm.

Emerson claimed that Aunt Lizzie wore false teeth, which I didn't believe for a minute. The only person I knew who had false teeth was old Herman from down the Northcote road. As his teeth clattered and roamed around his mouth so much, there was no mistake that the teeth were store-bought — the term for high-class dentistry in those days. Emerson and I had a terrible argument over the matter. I said I was sure he was wrong: I had never seen Aunt Lizzie without her teeth, and I doubted Emerson had either.

But Emerson was adamant that Aunt Lizzie took out her teeth every night and put them under the bible on the little table beside her bed in the back bedroom. He said he discovered this one night when he had peeked through the crack of the door as she was undressing: he had wanted to see if she really did have a hollow leg, as Father had dropped this bit of information one day when he was lamenting about all the food she could tuck away. I was relieved to hear that at least her legs were her own. And both Audrey and I were also sure that Emerson was mistaken about the teeth. Well, he was going to set out to prove us wrong. This alarmed me since, next to Ronny, my bad cousin from Montreal, Emerson could get into more trouble than anyone else I knew.

Aunt Lizzie loved to 'lay in late', as we called sleeping in. One day Emerson came to the breakfast table with a flushed face and darting eyes. His appearance immediately signaled to me that he had been up to some dastardly deed. Emerson hissed between clenched teeth that Audrey and I were to meet him in the drive-shed as soon as we had finished our porridge.

We gulped down our breakfast and tore outside, our winter coats tossed over our shoulders. The pocket of Emerson's breeks was bulging: he reached in to pull out something cupped in both hands, which could easily have been a dead mouse as Emerson loved to try this trick on us often. We hung back until he lifted one hand off the other. And there, before our eyes, was a set of false teeth.

"See, she has bottom ones and top ones." He was grinning from ear to ear, just as if he had discovered America. Audrey and I, who had never seen a set of false teeth before in our entire lives, moved closer but still kept our distance. I wasn't sure that the teeth might not reach up and snap at us. Once the shock wore off, the full impact of what he had done sunk in, and Audrey and I could think only of the consequences if Aunt Lizzie woke up early only to find her teeth weren't in their usual hiding place.

Emerson advised us not to be alarmed. Apparently, he had bunched up a piece of paper and slipped it under the Bible to make it look as if the teeth were still there. And, anyway, he was taking the teeth back as soon as we had a good look at them. Emerson asked us if we wanted to try them out, and he held them up to his mouth to show us how to put them in if we so desired. But Audrey said the best thing he could do was march right back upstairs and not say a word to anybody.

Unfortunately, Father saw us from the barn and yelled for Emerson to help with the chores immediately. A command from our father was always heeded on the spot, so Emerson thrust the teeth at Audrey and took off like someone possessed. We were left standing in the drive-shed with Aunt Lizzie's teeth.

As I had the same healthy respect for the teeth as I had for the shot gun that rested in the corner of the parlour, I would not for anything in the world touch them with a ten-foot pole. That left Audrey wondering how she was going to get them back upstairs without being noticed. Fortunately for us, Aunt Lizzie slept with black eye-patches, a lace night cap, and ear plugs. Audrey was able to sneak into the bedroom and replace the bundled-up paper with the teeth before she awakened.

I must confess, the discovery that Aunt Lizzie wasn't exactly perfect was a letdown to me. Even though she had perfect control over her false teeth — not once did I ever hear them clatter — I never quite viewed her in the same light again. Before, I used to spend every minute scrutinizing her pencilled, arched eyebrows and her shiny, rouged cheeks. But after it was proved that she wore false teeth, my line of vision settled around her mouth.

Now, I would have loved to try on the teeth. But I lacked Emerson's sense of adventure and I never would have dreamed of stealing them from the night table. And so, when Aunt Lizzie smiled at me and patted my hand — as she so often did — I was left wondering if she liked me enough that I might ask her one day to show me how she took them out and put them in. I never did ask her, naturally. I had to content myself with just viewing them in her mouth and wondering what kept them there.

The day of the Turkey Fair

It now seems to me that it took us forever to get ready for Turkey Fair day. The night before, Mother and Father got little sleep because they had to stay up to clean the last of the fowl, which included not only turkeys but chickens, ducks, and geese. And Audrey and I wrapped home-made bread and pounds of hand-churned butter long into the night as well.

We were all up at dawn, piling on long underwear and heavy knit vests and stockings so that when we finally had on our melton cloth coats and leggings, we looked like mummies.

It was important that we get to town early. The best spot on the main street was right in front of the Chinese restaurant as this was where the big-city wholesale buyers spent most of their time. The town buyers, too, seemed to congregate in front of the town's most popular eating spot. Because every farmer in the county wanted this vantage point, it meant that we had to be on the road for the twelve-mile trek to town by six o'clock in the morning.

Audrey and I sat on the straw bed with our feet against the backs of our brothers. Between us and our parents, who sat on the only seat at the front of the sleigh, were our wares. They were lined up like soldiers and lay between clean, white sheets. Quilts and blankets covered the wares to prevent them from freezing. Audrey and I held the lunch, which our family would eat in the Chinese restaurant: unless a city buyer came along and bought your entire load, you were likely to be in town most of the day. On Mother's lap were an old, worn, leather purse, which had come in a box of hand-me-downs from Aunt Lizzie, and a small, draw-string bag made of flour-bag cotton — it was to hold the money. Just before she climbed on the sleigh seat Mother had said, "Please God, may it be full to brimming." We were accustomed to her talks to God, which took place frequently and as if no one else was listening.

The day was the most bitter of days in December. When we arrived, other farmers were just starting to pull into town. Father had the horses at a good trot and, as luck would have it, a truck was just pulling out of the curb in front of the restaurant. Father steered the sleigh into the spot. Everett unhitched the team and took the horses to the town stable where they would stay for the day.

It was a day when we children were allowed to wander the town streets in happy abandon. There wasn't a store that didn't escape our careful scrutiny, but the five-and-dime received the most attention. This was the closest we were ever going to get to big, store-bought, slate blackboards and sleighs with steel runners, and the countless other things that were beyond the reach of most farm children who grew up during the Depression.

We had discovered that if we went into the restaurant just a few minutes before noon, we were apt to get a good seat. The owners didn't seem to mind that we had brought our lunch from home. And because money flowed with a little more ease on Turkey Fair day than was usual, we were allowed to buy a soft drink to have with our sandwiches. As was her custom, Mother would reach down inside the white, draw-string bag, take out a few coins, and give them to Audrey, who was the oldest and considered the most responsible. It was Audrey's task to see that the drinks got paid for.

On this day, Mother went to the blankets on the sleigh to get the bag. We saw her frantically toss things about; her face was flushed and her eyes were wild. The bag was gone. Father joined the search, and we children were sick with fear that the bag was gone forever. I began to cry, which Audrey said was just making things worse. Emerson had already gone into the restaurant to hold a seat.

The bag was nowhere in sight. Mother opened the old, leather purse and took out a quarter. We were told to share a drink. With leaded feet we entered the restaurant carrying the brown paper bag of sandwiches; Father remained behind to search under the sleigh, his knees in the snow. As we opened the restaurant door, Mother's last words were, "Months of work for nothing. Dear God, help us find it."

Barely a word was spoken in the restaurant. The sandwiches tasted like wood chips, and we decided not to buy a drink after all. But then we noticed some excitement at the counter: more farmers were coming in and a woman from town who had been buying on the street had a brown paper bag, which she was opening at the counter. She took out what we recognized was

Mother's hand-made money bag. We overheard her say that it had been wrapped up with her chicken and butter. Emerson flew out of the seat, and we saw the restaurant door slam against the wall. Mother was inside in seconds. She showed the woman where she had put a button on the top of the bag in case the draw-string failed. And from the look of relief on her face, it was obvious to everyone our mother was the rightful owner of the little bag of money.

Mother didn't care who was listening. Right then and there she thanked God for finding the bag, and Audrey even joined in the loud amen. Back in the thirties, to be anything less than honest was unheard of. Mother dragged the woman outside and wrapped up another chicken for her and added a loaf of bread and a pound of fresh butter.

Then she tore back into the restaurant and put a whole dollar bill in front of Audrey. We could each have our own bottle of cream soda. There was even enough money left over to buy a big dish of ice cream — and we asked for five spoons with which to eat it. There was probably enough that we could have each had our own cone. But there was no sense in being completely frivolous. After all, there was a Depression on.

IF IT WASN'T FOR TURKEY FAIR DAY, THERE WOULD BE LITTLE OR NO EXTRA CASH FOR CHRISTMAS. IT WAS WONDERFUL IF ONE OF THE BIG PACKERS BOUGHT A FARMER'S ENTIRE LOAD EARLY IN THE MORNING. BUT AS THIS DIDN'T HAPPEN OFTEN, TURKEY FAIR DAY USUALLY SAW US ON RENFREW'S MAIN STREET FROM DAWN TO DUSK.

The tooth fairy

Although I had never seen her, I was absolutely positive the tooth fairy existed. Being blessed with a vivid imagination as a child, I created this mythical being in my mind with such detail that I was certain I could reach out and touch her.

The tooth fairy wore a blue gossamer gown to which were attached sheer wings; she had long, golden hair and carried a wand with a star on the end; she also had tied to her wrist a little bag of silk that was full of gold coins. In this bag it was the pennies that, by some miracle, came to be found under my pillow the morning after I had relinquished a baby tooth amid much commotion and tears.

I never stopped to consider that the bag held only gold coins and what I found was either copper pennies or a shiny, silver nickel. As was my habit, if some fantasy didn't fit into my scheme of things I simply changed it around until it did. Thus, I naturally thought the gold coin was transformed when it touched the feather pillow. This theory suited my purpose very well.

One bitterly cold Sunday — a day I remember distinctly — my faith in the tooth fairy was severely tested. We had skated on the Bonnechere all afternoon and indulged in a favourite pastime of eating pieces of chipped ice that had been kicked up by our skates. I bit hard on one chunk and felt my front baby tooth move like a pivot. I even saw a few drops of blood on my fingers. Screaming every inch of the way, I tore back to the house with my frozen mitt clamped over my mouth.

Father was sitting at the Findlay Oval with his stockinged feet up on the oven door when I hit the kitchen like a cyclone. Seeing that the tooth was hanging by a thread, he said he would just have a look at how much of it was still anchored. I roared as if I was being stabbed as his fingers wrapped around the little tooth, and then it was in his hand. I ran to look in the mirror at the great, gaping hole in my mouth.

Mother said that, if I wrapped the tooth in a hanky and put it under my pillow before bedtime, she was sure the tooth fairy would make her usual trip in the night. But I made the mistake of showing the tooth to my brothers and sister when they came in from skating. When I said the tooth fairy might even leave a dime since I was older than the last time I had lost a tooth, my brother Emerson immediately doubled over with laughter. "Don't count on it," he said, belittling my excitement.

The outdoors and the exercise contributed to my falling asleep almost as soon as my head hit the pillow, under which the baby tooth was wrapped in my best Sunday hanky. Emerson had made several hateful comments, but these had fallen on deaf ears.

The next morning I woke with that wonderful feeling of excitement I always had when I knew something marvellous was about to happen. The bedroom was ice cold, and I could see my breath. I reached under my pillow for the hanky, but instead my hand closed around a paper bag. It was hard as a rock. For a fleeting moment I wondered if the tooth fairy had changed her givings. I sat up in bed and opened the bag. I could not believe what I saw. Inside was a horse bun, frozen solid with bits of ice around it, pointing to the fact that it had been picked up in the yard and very recently, too.

I scrunched the bag tight and, paying no mind to the icy floor, stepped over my felt slippers and tore downstairs like someone possessed. All the brothers were in from doing the early morning chores and Audrey was making school lunches while Mother was sorting clothes for the usual Monday morning washing.

I marched right up to Emerson and thrust the bag in his face. He looked the picture of innocence. "Sure doesn't look like a dime to me," he said as he continued to eat his rolled oats. I took the bag to Mother, who gave it not more than a quick glance. "Throw that thing outside, Mary," she said. "Whatever are you doing with something like manure in a brown paper bag in the house, for goodness' sake?" Even Father, who thought the situation was rather comical, told me to get rid of it. I demanded to know what had happened to my money that had been left by the tooth fairy, whereupon Emerson said, "Well, I guess she ran out, that's all."

After tossing the horse bun outside, I searched the bed. Nothing. Only my good hanky was lying on the mat. I went down to the breakfast table and openly accused Emerson of the dastardly deed. His eyes opened in mock horror: "Me? Why do you always think it is me?"

I put on my most severe look by squinting my eyes almost shut tight and talking through clenched teeth, a trick I had learned from that hateful Marguerite, a classmate at the Northcote school. But my attitude cut no ice with Emerson. He emphatically denied doing the deed. To this day he vows he has no idea how the manure got under my pillow.

For some time after this incident, I remember not having much faith in the tooth fairy. But with the very next baby tooth I lost, she returned. And I know not whether Mother intervened, or whether Emerson just had a sudden stroke of compassion.

MOTHER WITH HER BOYS — EMERSON, EARL, AND EVERETT DRESSED FOR CHURCH IN THEIR SUNDAY BEST.

The joy of Christmas

Christmas Day traditionally began very early on our farm in Renfrew County in the thirties. Before we were allowed near the Christmas tree, we had the barn chores to do — although I suspect they were done in a careless fashion for once. To further prolong the agony of waiting for our gifts, Mother insisted that each of us eat a good, hearty breakfast. This usually meant porridge, eggs, and toast. And then we were expected to clean up the kitchen.

It seems to me that we had a couple of hours under our belts by the time we were finally allowed near the tree. There is no need to mention that in the thirties, when money was so scarce, our Christmas gifts were of the simplest kind. Indeed, anyone who grew up during the Depression has his own memories of those hard times. Yet, Christmas was always a joyous occasion: it didn't matter what was or wasn't under the tree. Each of us usually received one bought toy — one that could be shared with all the members of the family — and then there were items that our Mother would have made for us. Aprons, which I found most distasteful, were one of her favourite gifts. Father would often make wooden bird-houses or home-made sleighs, which we thought were wonderful.

The only candy we ever had during Christmas was the few, hard, striped peppermints found in the bottom of our stockings. And usually an orange was tucked in, too. This was a rare treat, as fresh, imported fruit never found its way to our dining table at any other time of the year.

There was no ripping off of gift paper. The parcels had to be carefully unwrapped, and ribbons, if any, had to be handed over to Mother before they could get mixed up with the boxes and discards, which would be thrown into the cook-stove to burn. Before the day was out, our mother would iron the Christmas paper and ribbon, which would be carefully tucked away until the next year. To this day, my hand trembles when I see anyone rip off gift paper with no thought of re-using it. I want to retrieve it, iron out its wrinkles, and save it for another day.

Christmas dinner, however, was no different than it is today. But we always ate our big meal at noon hour. This was because, as long as I can remember, the afternoon was spent entertaining friends and neighbours who came to call. Our big, old, country farmhome seemed to be the gathering place and, come early afternoon, the first sleigh load would arrive — children, parents, and grandparents — until the old house was bursting at its log seams. My mother would play the harmonica or the pump organ, my brother Earl and I would do Scottish dancing, and without too much coaxing I would recite a couple of monologues, which Mother would have written for me.

About mid-afternoon, when the adults were settling back in their chairs for a good, old, country visit, we young folks got bundled up in our melton cloth slacks and heavy coats and, with our skates tied to our feet, made our way to the river. There, for the next couple of hours, we skated to our hearts' content. The home-made sleighs got their first outings, too. And, if the snow was crusty, we used huge cardboard boxes to slide down the hill — four or five of us piling in and flying down past the cedar cluster and on over the frozen river. It was a glorious, fun time: the very young children mixed with the teenagers so naturally and happily, as we all took part in the activities of the day.

Oncoming darkness would drive us, with scarlet cheeks and weary bodies, from the river and the hill and back to the house. The adults would gather together their little ones, often leaving their skates on for the ride home. That night we would be exhausted from the day's events, and when we climbed the stairs for bed it was with the utmost contentment and happiness. The Depression meant nothing to us young folks for wealth was being happy and healthy with loved ones around to share the joy.

Icebox duties

How well off I thought we were back in the thirties just because we were proud owners of an icebox. It was a narrow cabinet, made from highly polished oak, with steel-lined doors and ice-bin. As the ice melted, a small tube carried the water to a pan, which sat on the floor under the icebox. The pan had to be emptied several times a day, depending on the season. In the winter, we would get away with emptying it morning and night but, in the summer, it had to be done more often.

My job involved seeing that the pan never overflowed — and heaven help me if it did. Depending on how stressed Mother's day had been, for letting the pan overflow I would either get a few, hard scuts on the behind and made to clean up the mess or I would get the same long dialogue on responsibility that was delivered most times I failed to meet my obligations. I was only six or seven years old but, nonetheless, as with my three brothers and sister, I was expected to have the common sense to do my daily chores without being reminded.

The big blocks of ice were kept in the ice-house, which was located at the north side of the barn so it would receive as much protection from the sun as possible. It was the brothers' job to bring the blocks into the house, ridding them of the coating of sawdust before doing so. We had large, black iron tongs that weighed as much as the block of ice, but my brothers seemed to manage them without too much difficulty.

Sometimes it became impossible for me to remember all that I was expected to do, and I would forget. I tried my utmost every morning and every night to run over the chores in my mind. I can remember thinking of all the chores I had to finish just before I crawled between the feather tickings. But, invariably, I would forget some task. The consequences were not always pleasant.

For some reason that to this day I can't explain I often forgot to empty the ice-pan. Sometimes Audrey would remind me, but she had enough chores of her own. I forgot to do this chore one bitterly cold winter night and the next morning that corner of the kitchen was covered with water. Moreover, because the house had no insulation, the baseboards were covered with frost and the ice water froze the big, braided rug to the wall. Mother had to pour boiling water on it to free it. This lapse of memory did not sit kindly with her, and I can remember having to go to bed early that night to pay for my forgetfulness.

In the summer, the pan had to be emptied several times a day. I soon got in the habit of checking it every time I went into the house because the pan was much easier to empty if it wasn't full to the brim.

My brother Emerson, who used to haunt my earlier life, knew I had a hard time remembering to empty the ice-basin. And, because I knew he was a tyrant, I realized that even if he saw the water starting to run over onto the floor he wouldn't have the decency to tell me. As if this wasn't bad enough, Emerson also took special delight in stocking the pan with long dew worms or dead mice. Once he even put a huge toad in the pan, but was found out when the toad escaped and it took three of us to catch it.

Because of Emerson's bent for mischief, I kept a wary eye on him when he was in the kitchen. But he had an uncanny way of doing things unnoticed. I never knew what I was going to find when I pulled the ice-pan out from under the box.

I tried to trade jobs with my sister, Audrey — but to no avail. There were some jobs she hated as much as I, but apparently not enough to trade with me. The ice-pan remained my job as long as we lived on the farm.

Even though I hated looking after the melted ice water, I was astute enough to know that we were very fortunate to have an icebox. Very few homes I knew in the township had one. A little brass plate on the top door proved it was made by the Barnett Company in Renfrew. The icebox didn't come our way as most things did back in the thirties — by trading farm produce or loads of gravel. My grandfather bought it for us. One day, like a bolt out of the blue, he arrived from Ottawa in his Ford rumble seat car and told my father to hitch up the wagon as we were going into Renfrew to buy an icebox. It was that simple. Perhaps Grandfather's meticulous nature found something unsavoury about the swinging shelf in the cellar that held our perishables, or perhaps he felt sorry for our mother who had few modern trappings on our Renfrew County farm.

When the shiny, oak Barnett icebox was unloaded off the wagon (that summer we had to buy ice from the one neighbour we knew who had one too), I felt our stature in the township grew. Now my worst enemy at the Northcote school, Marguerite, could brag all she wanted about her inside bathroom. ***We*** had an icebox. For me, that was far more prestigious than a flush toilet that froze in the winter.

GRANDFATHER WITH ONE OF HIS MANY CARS. ALTHOUGH HE OWNED CARS OF ALMOST EVERY TYPE AND DESCRIPTION, I WAS ESPECIALLY FOND OF THE FORD WITH THE RUMBLE SEAT.

A New York Christmas

When my mother moved to the farm in the backwoods of Ontario after living for eighteen years in the heart of New York, she made a valiant attempt at keeping in touch with her beloved city — if not in body at least in heart and spirit. She managed this in several ways, one of which was to retain the customs of her childhood days.

It was Christmas, and in the thirties the Depression was carrying on its quiet war all around us. But Mother was able to bring to our isolated farm the joy of the season and to build for us a legacy of fond memories.

The spruce tree had been cut several days before. It was hauled into the summer kitchen, and we five children watched as our father took the broom to the branches to dislodge every last clump of snow that clung stubbornly to its boughs. It was then dragged into the big room that served as both kitchen and living room. The old pine table was moved away from the west wall to make room for the tree, which was at least eight feet tall.

"In New York we always had the tree in front of a window so that people could see it from the outside," my mother said. Father paused for just a moment, "And who do you think is going to see the tree from outside? The cows mebbe?" So the tree, which was planted in a wash-tub filled with sand, was placed in a corner. Chicken wire anchored it to the wall and the ceiling.

For weeks we had been hearing what a lean Christmas it was going to be. The leanest yet. There would be little money for toys and certainly no money for tree decorations. We had made popcorn balls and paper links. These we hung on the tree, but still it was bare beyond belief. We surveyed it sadly. But then our mother vanished upstairs and brought down what she called the under-the-bed box. It was, in fact, a large coat box, with Gimbles written across it in bold letters. As to its contents we were ignorant. We only knew that this box was "private". Under no circumstances were we to go into it.

We gathered round the old pine table and watched as Mother carefully lifted the lid. Lo and behold, inside were all the decorations she had brought with her from New York. They weren't elaborate, but there were pieces of fruit and vegetables made of felt and embroidered in silver thread — and for the top of the tree was a white angel with outstretched arms and cherub face. They had been wrapped carefully in a copy of the *Philadelphia Enquirer*, my mother's favourite newspaper. When she laid out the decorations on the table, we thought they were the most beautiful sight we had ever seen.

We wanted to know why they had not been brought out in past years. Mother told us that there seemed to be no need for them before, but ***this*** particular year had been a struggle and she had known that Christmas was going to be lean. "It seemed to be the right year for the New York decorations to come out of hiding," she said.

Soon the last decoration was hung, and we stood back and admired the sight. We were sure it was now the nicest Christmas tree in Renfrew County.

Later my mother went to the side-board, got out her harmonica, and settled herself into the old rocking chair. This was our cue to sit around her knee on the floor. I can remember how Mother would give the harmonica a few sharp raps on the palm of her hand and run it up and down the scale just "to make sure all the notes were still there," she'd say, giving a deep wink.

We sang Christmas carols — all the old favourites. And, even though the song had nothing whatever to do with the Christmas season, my mother ended the sing-song — as she always did — with "The Sidewalks of New York". This was a final tribute to the beloved city she had left behind.

A Christmas wish gone awry

Miss Crosby, who taught at the Northcote school, decided early in December that we would all write letters to Santa and send them off to the *Ottawa Farm Journal* where, three times a week, the best were chosen for publication. She thought the exercise would be a valuable lesson in penmanship, on which she placed great emphasis, and would teach us at the same time about the value of good citizenship. In our letters we were to not only tell Santa what we wanted to find under the Christmas tree on Christmas morning, but also to write what we would do to better our country and the community in which we lived.

Marguerite hadn't been so excited since she was chosen to present a bouquet of flowers to the wife of the chairman of the Board of Education at the box social one summer! She was absolutely positive her letter would be published. Miss Crosby had said that each of us would be required to read our letters to the school before they were mailed off in a big, brown envelope to the *Ottawa Farm Journal*. Marguerite was squirming in her seat as if she were sitting on a dozen oranges. I could hardly concentrate on my own letter for watching her.

I decided, as usual, to ask for a doll. Only this time I asked that it have new clothes, not ones that had been made out of the same material as my pyjamas and pinnies. Since there wasn't much chance that I would be getting my wish, I also asked for a new bookbag and a diary with a lock and key.

We all had diaries at home as Mother insisted we write down our daily thoughts just after we finished our homework at night. But we used small, five-cent scribblers, and I know for an absolute fact that my brother Emerson read mine from cover to cover when he was alone in the upstairs bedroom. How else would he know that I secretly wanted to grow up to dance on a New York stage and sing in a vaudeville show? I wanted a diary that was little and covered in satin and that had a lock clasp and a gold key. I even told Santa I would be much obliged if the cover could be blue taffeta like one I had seen in the dime store in Renfrew.

Just as it was no problem to write down my Christmas wish, it was also no problem to write what I wished Santa would do for our country. I wanted him to get rid of the Depression. How he was going to accomplish this I did not know. This I would leave to his powers of magic. In my letter I wrote at great length of all the things I knew about the Depression, things that I had overheard my parents say when they were downstairs in the kitchen and I had supposedly gone to bed. I figured that if I could eliminate those worries for them, I would be benefitting all of Renfrew County.

When it came time to read our letters out to the whole school, I found that most of us had asked for the same wish — that is, all except Marguerite. She had wished for a new schoolhouse, one with running water and a flush toilet like she had at her house. She just ***had*** to throw this in, I suppose, since she constantly talked about how well off her family was and that her house was one of the few in the entire township that boasted an inside bathroom.

The letters were pushed into the big, brown envelope, and Miss Crosby said she would mail them from Briscoe's store on her way home. She also said that she was sure one or two would be picked to run in the *Ottawa Farm Journal*.

We watched the paper daily like hawks. There were letters from children in Ottawa, Renfrew, and a place called Prescott, which we had never heard of. We had just about given up hope when Miss Crosby came into school one day with the *Ottawa Farm Journal* folded under her arm. She told us that three of our letters had been chosen for the Santa Claus page.

Miss Crosby kept us in suspense until after prayers, the bible reading, and the singing of "God Save the King". Then she opened the paper on her desk. We were told to form a line and come up two at a time to read the letters. (Miss Crosby was great for regimentation: there was no such thing as wandering aimlessly up to the front of the room.) As I was in a junior grade, I was one of the first in line.

You can imagine my excitement when I saw my name at the bottom of a letter — and right beside was Marguerite's. Our ages, seven years old, were in brackets underneath our letters. But to my absolute horror, through some fluke of the presses, my name had appeared under Marguerite's letter and hers under mine! There I was asking for an inside bathroom in the Northcote school and raving about the one we had at our home. Marguerite was just as upset to be asking Santa for something as silly as a blue taffeta diary.

Everyone in the school thought the mix-up was hilarious. But I thought it was the worst calamity that had ever befallen me. I couldn't understand how a big city newspaper like the *Ottawa Farm Journal* could have made such a mistake. It took most of the morning for Miss Crosby to calm both of us down.

I would like to say that Santa was able to sort the whole thing out on Christmas. But Marguerite did not get a new schoolhouse with an inside privy; I did not get a taffeta-bound diary. And, as everyone knows, Santa did little to eliminate the ravages of the Depression, which was with us for many years after the letter had appeared in the *Ottawa Farm Journal*.

IN THIS PICTURE OF SOME OF MY SCHOOLMATES AT THE NORTHCOTE SCHOOL, I CAN BE FOUND STANDING DIRECTLY BEHIND THE LITTLE GIRL IN THE WHITE FUR COAT.

Audrey's singing debut

My sister, Audrey, who was the oldest sibling in our family, was tall and slender. Mounds of jet black hair swirled around her face like great clouds of silk. Audrey's eyes were just as dark, and she had the high cheekbones so prevalent among the German people of that part of the Ottawa Valley.

I thought Audrey was quite beautiful. As well as having a goodly portion of the beauty that God handed out to our family, she was also blessed with a sweet singing voice, which, when the spirit moved her, would ring out loud and clear through the house like so many bells on a frosty morning. Mother said she sang like an angel and looked like an angel. I could never understand this as the angels I had seen in our old family Bible had cascades of golden curls pouring down their backs, fair skin, and small, round faces. As far as I was concerned, my dark-skinned, black-haired sister was the farthest thing from an angel anyone could be.

Mother thought it was time Audrey made her singing debut in church. The brothers howled with laughter at this suggestion. Every time Audrey raised her voice in song, in a pretense of going deaf from the noise, they would slap their hands over their ears and run for cover. So the thought of their sister singing in church sent them into spasms of glee. Only a sound cuff on the side of their heads by Mother silenced them once and for all.

Audrey was appalled at the thought of singing in church. Around the kitchen on a Saturday morning was fine, or even walking to school with several of the neighbour's children in tow — but getting up in front of a silent congregation on a Sunday morning was quite another thing.

Nevertheless, Mother spoke to the minister, who conferred with the crotchety organist, and the die was cast. Audrey was to practise a piece she liked, but she protested there wasn't one hymn in the whole book of which she was especially fond. But Mother accepted no excuses. Any chance she had of promoting the talents of one of her brood, she did so. It mattered little what the child thought of the whole deal. It was this same attitude that was behind my dancing on every stage in Renfrew County and the brothers acting out one-act plays at every opportunity. Here was a chance for another child to show her talents: Audrey had not a hope in the world of getting out of it.

My heart ached for her. I remember it was in the middle of winter — not an unusually severe winter as winters go in the Valley — and Audrey insisted that I get down on my knees with her beside the bed the week of her performance and pray for such a blizzard that every Lutheran in the Northcote area would be forced to stay home. Now, the truth of the matter was that even the fiercest of winter storms never kept anyone home from church. If you had to crawl hip deep in snow, you made it. So I knew our prayers were in vain, but I went along with her to quell the fear in her heart.

Twice during that week Audrey was driven to church after school to practise with the organist. Although Mother assured all of us that she was getting along just beautifully, each night after supper she had my sister stand before us and, while she played softly on the harmonica, Audrey went over her selection. Mother made sure that Audrey stood with her both feet tight together and that she placed her hands together like two leaves inside each other.

Sunday broke sunny and crispy cold — just a perfect day for a good, big crowd at church, noted Audrey when she awoke. She had slept in rags all night, and Mother combed her already naturally curly hair into puffy ringlets, which swirled around her face like a fur collar. Just before we went out the door, Mother dabbed a bit of Tanjay face powder on her flushed cheeks. The brothers snickered behind their hands. But when Mother shot them a look that would wither a grape, they regained their composure in a hurry.

It came time for Audrey's debut. The minister simply smiled and nodded in Audrey's direction, and I must say I was heartily disappointed that he didn't call out her name and say she was the talented sister of Mary Haneman. Audrey went up and stood beside the old pump organ. I could see her shift her feet so that they were both planted tightly side by side. Then she deliberately placed one cupped hand inside the other and her eyes found a spot on one of the big oak rafters in the ceiling.

With the first note of the organ, Audrey's round mouth formed the words, but not a sound came out. The organist was quick and played another few bars, and once again nodded in my sister's direction. This time the first note rang out loud and clear like so many bells, and I could see beside me my mother's shoulders relax.

I stole a glance at my brothers, who were suddenly in awe of the whole performance. Even the minister's wife, who rarely took her eyes off a certain spot beside the pulpit, was misty-eyed and beaming in Audrey's direction. The words poured out and filled the church. I noticed that Audrey's hands relaxed a bit and that she let her eyes slide over the congregation just as Mother had instructed her to do.

When she finished there was a hush over the church. For a few seconds I thought she had put the minister to sleep because he moved not a muscle. Then he rose and said Audrey sang beautifully. He hoped she would sing often. There were congratulations all around when we came out of church, and it looked very much as if my sister, the soloist, was launched. Mother and Father were so proud that they did something they rarely did on a Sunday: they stopped at Briscoe's store on the way home and bought five ice cream cones. After all, it wasn't every day a member of the family sang solo in church.

AUDREY ON THE DAY SHE LEFT TO WORK IN TOWN. SHE LASTED ONE WEEK AS SHE WAS TOO LONESOME FOR HOME.

My father's gold watch

Father was especially proud of his gold watch. He was never quite sure where it came from, but he thought perhaps his grandfather had brought it from Germany. He sometimes wore it to church but preferred to wear it only to weddings and funerals. Occasions, he said, were more befitting the likes of a gold watch and chain.

The watch sat in a sugar bowl in the kitchen cupboard between wearings. Every second day or so, Father would take it out, wind it, put it to his ear, and then pop it back in the bowl. We always said that, next to his children and his pipe, Father loved his gold watch best.

There was one winter — referred to in our family as the winter of the gold watch — I remember well. It was when the drifts were sky high and, as Mother often said, so were the bills. Father mentioned he would soon have to supplement the fast dwindling grain in the barn, and he had no idea where the money was going to come from.

But always when things seemed blackest, when there wasn't another penny to be fished out of the teapot, something or someone always came along to give us sustenance for another spell. Mother called it the divine hand of providence.

One Saturday the picker drove into the yard on his long box sleigh. He had a nose like a hawk and wore a voluminous raccoon coat with a hugh collar that all but obscured his head. The picker drove from farm to farm buying up whatever anyone wanted to sell. We exchanged animal hides, old harness, brass bells, wooden buckets, and anything else that we felt we could get along without for a few dollars, dollars that would see us through another crisis.

When he drove into the yard and lumbered through the snow to our kitchen door, Mother had already scanned the kitchen to see what we could part with. Father sent Everett scurrying to the barn for two cowhides that had been cured and were just waiting for the picker. As the picker had his eye on the old potash pot that was at the corner of the house, Father said this might be as good a day as any to get rid of it.

Finally the sleigh was loaded, and the man was completing his transaction at the kitchen table with us five children gathered round. We watched him peel off a bill from a roll the likes of which we only saw whenever he came to the farm. Father looked at the few dollars, and we all knew that he was mentally weighing them against the bills we owed.

Father's eyes roamed the kitchen again. We had already parted with our best coal oil lamp on an earlier visit. Then his eyes came to rest on the sugar bowl. Mother barely whispered, "No, Albert," but he was already at the cupboard door. "Solid gold," Father said, fingering his prized watch. The man with the hawk nose rolled it around in his hand: "Can't get much for those these days. Nobody wants a gold watch anymore, it seems. About all I could give you would be a couple of dollars." "Five and you can have it," Father said. "Four," said the picker. "It's yours," and Father handed over the watch.

Then, without another word, Father put on his coat and hat and headed for the barn. The picker was gathering up the few possessions he was able to negotiate for at our kitchen table. Mother looked at him pocket the watch. "I'll buy it back," she said. "What with?" the picker asked. "I imagine I can come up with four dollars' worth of things you would like to have." "Oh, the price is five now," he said.

Mother took the picker upstairs to the trunk in the front hall. It was full of memories she had brought with her from her beloved New York City. The picker's eyes shone like jewels as he watched her bring out treasure after treasure: a linen tablecloth, a bolt of pure silk material, and a small statue of the Empire State Building. "I figure you have more than five dollars' worth there," she said. The old man never took his eyes off the trunk, but Mother slammed the lid down with a thump and barely missed his fingers that were prodding its contents.

That night, when Father came in for supper, the gold watch was sitting on his plate. He never asked what mother had to trade to get it back. He knew she was a tough negotiator, and he doubted the picker got the best of the bargain. He put it back in the sugar bowl in the cupboard. But, thereafter, Father didn't save the gold watch for funerals and weddings. Every Sunday he took it out, rubbed it on the tail of his jacket, and popped it into his vest pocket.

When New Year's Eve came early

It was the first year I remember that my Montreal cousins were to be with us over the Christmas and New Year's holidays. In spite of the fact that they would have had many more gifts had they stayed in the city, they had elected to stay with us out on our farm in Renfrew County. I remember the snow was piled sky-high that year and it was the kind of holiday season I recall with great fondness.

In that part of the Ottawa Valley it wasn't customary to make too much fuss over New Year's Eve because, regardless how late you stayed up, you still had to get out to the barn before daybreak and tend to the livestock. Any thought of celebrating New Year's Eve soon lost its appeal when we considered what lay ahead of us in the morning. My mother, however, having lived in New York City before coming to the Renfrew County farm, missed the frivolity of the holiday season and often lamented that, in her mind, the Valley people certainly didn't do much to welcome in a new year. She really couldn't see how the cows would suffer if they weren't milked at the crack of dawn. But, until that year when our Montreal cousins stayed over, Mother never belaboured the point, and Father always won out with his reasonings that farm chores came first.

I really don't remember whose idea it was that we all stay up to see in the New Year. But, sitting around the kitchen table with less than six hours left to the old year, someone had mentioned that since Ronny and Terry were with us this might be a good year to stay up until midnight. My mother thought this was a wonderful idea. I was less than enthusiastic since I was usually ready for bed by eight o'clock, which meant that the rest of the children had to follow soon after.

My father thought this was the craziest notion he had ever heard of and said, "It makes no matter to me if yer fool enough to stay up to midnight. But I'll tell you one thing fer sure, you'll all be up as usual at six."

The thought of the late night, however, and the fun that lay ahead over-ruled everything else. And so it was decided we would all see in the new year, with the exception of Father, of course, who was already stoking the stove and drinking his final cup of green tea.

Mother got things off to a rousing start by leading us all in a sing-song. All went well until my brother Emerson decided he could sing in harmony; of course, he threw everyone off key because, even under ideal conditions such as in the church choir, Emerson had a less-than-perfect singing voice. We all started to laugh at the discord, which threw him into a rage and he punched my sister such a whollop that she fell off her chair. Mother said we had had enough singing.

Musical chairs was a long-time favourite at any social gathering in the thirties, and we swung into the game after the sing-song, with Mother on the harmonica. If you remember the game, you will know there is always someone left without a seat when the music stops.

The game had eliminated everyone but Ronny and Emerson, and they were running around the one chair so fast we could hardly see their legs moving. Mother had turned her back so as not to show any partiality. Ronny soon found out that the only way to win was to pick up the chair and run with it, which certainly was a new twist to the game and not exactly Emerson's idea of good sportsmanship.

What developed was the worst incident of name-calling I have ever heard. The music stopped, Ronny dropped the chair and threw himself onto the seat with such an impact the legs almost buckled, then Emerson flung himself on top of Ronny, demanding that he be recognized as the winner. The screaming could be heard in Admaston, I am sure. Only for the fact that my mother grabbed each by an ear, I think there surely would have been blood shed.

It took Father about ten seconds to make it to the bottom of the staircase. There he stood in his long, fleece-lined underwear and, one arm flung high in the air, he shouted, "Enough. Enough. To bed, all of you. Can't a man get any rest around here with daylight just around the corner?" My mother was putting her harmonica back in its blue velvet box. It looked as if she was relieved that he had intervened.

When we climbed the stairs for bed that night, I noticed that the old gingerbread clock on the shelf in the kitchen said half past eight. Our New Year's Eve party had lasted exactly forty-five minutes.

The big deceit

Being the younger sister, I was rarely taken into Audrey's confidence, especially when very personal subjects, such as sex and boys, were discussed. So, you can imagine my excitement when one day Audrey, in the most confidential of tones, whispered that she had something important she wanted to discuss with me.

I couldn't imagine what this could be. My young mind fantacized over every delicious subject I could think of. Perhaps one of Audrey's friends had got 'in trouble', as we called it in the thirties. Or perhaps Audrey was in love — but she didn't even have a boyfriend, so this possibility seemed highly unlikely. So I just had to wait until bedtime when, in the confines of our own room, Audrey had promised to share with me this most mysterious of topics.

Audrey prolonged my agony by insisting that we get undressed first. She peeled down to her long underwear and wool undershirt and took the oil lamp, which she turned up high and put close to the mirror over our washstand. She then turned sideways and looked at herself for a long period of time. Suddenly, Audrey asked me, "What do you see?" I was mystified. "Nothing," I retorted. "Exactly," Audrey said in the most baleful of tones.

I was having a great deal of difficulty in following the conversation. "Have you noticed the Thom girls?" she asked. Well, of course I noticed the Thom girls: they lived on the farm next to ours; we were all best friends; we saw them every day of our lives. I thought Audrey had taken leave of her senses. I had heard of young girls who suddenly went mad for no reason at all, and I was beginning to wonder if Audrey was one of these.

Audrey ran her opened hand over her bony chest. "Nothing," she repeated, and I thought she was going to cry. I looked down at my own long-sleeved undershirt. Although Audrey was about nine years older, we were built almost the same — every rib showing, and not much else.

Audrey set her jaw, as she always did when she was determined to change the course of events to her liking. "Tomorrow," she said, "you are going to see a big change." I wondered how she could develop her chest overnight, but I dared not throw out any doubts in case she shut me out of this discussion, which I was beginning to enjoy thoroughly.

My sister dropped to her knees and reached under the bed. She pulled out a handful of flour bags that had been torn into long, wide strips. Then she yanked off her undershirt. No, our chests certainly weren't much different. Audrey had a handful of big safety pins, which she placed on the washstand. She made me stand behind her, and she began to wrap her bony frame in the cotton strips. Around and around her body went the long pieces, and my job was to pin them together. When she had used up all the pieces, she took two small squares of cotton and scrunched them into lumps. These she forced down into the bindings. Again she went to the washstand mirror and scrutinized herself from every angle. "Now you hold them tight while I pull on my undershirt." I could see why I was taken into her confidence. This was one job Audrey would never have been able to do alone.

We worked the shirt over the rags, and then Audrey pulled on a sweater to see the effect. She looked like she had grown about four inches up top. I remarked that her body certainly didn't look much like the Thom girls' bodies to me. She glared at me and said she thought it looked fine to her. She decided to go to bed with the sweater on so as to be ready for school the next morning. I wondered about the wisdom of that but thought better of voicing an opinion.

Audrey stretched out like a mummy. The last time I stole a glance she was sleeping soundly with her hands folded gently over the two lumps under her sweater.

The next morning was bitterly cold when we wakened. Audrey groped for a match to light the still-dark room. She went right to the mirror and immediately turned sideways. It was obvious that something terrible had happened through the night. She was once again as flat as a tin plate. But her waist had expanded considerably. She raised the sweater and undershirt. The two balls of cotton fell to the floor, and the endless strips of flour bagging that we had so painstakingly wrapped around her chest the night before were now sitting on the waistband of her long underwear.

Audrey ripped off the bands without even stopping to open the pins, which flew in every direction. I quickly gathered up the scraps and tossed them under the bed. She wore a look of total dejection, and I thought if I offered one word of sympathy she would cry.

That day at school I couldn't take my eyes off the Thom girls. I secretly wondered if they were properly endowed, of if they had discovered a better method than wrapping strips of flour bags around their chests. I thought it would make Audrey feel better if I offered the opinion that I doubted very much if their figures were perfectly natural. I made up my mind that I would even lie if I had to and say that I saw safety pins through their blouses. After all, Audrey and I were sharing secrets now for the first time in my life. And I was going to do everything I could to keep this new relationship going.

AUDREY WAS SEVENTEEN WHEN THIS PICTURE WAS TAKEN. SHE HAD LONG SINCE CEASED TO NEED TO AUGMENT HER UPPER MIDRIFF WITH RAGS.

Tacks and cat-o'-nine-tails

Cecil, a Northcote schoolmate of many years ago, did much to make our public school days full of excitement, fun, and often anxiety. We all thought he wasn't very bright. However, time proved us wrong. Only after we had all grown up and left school did we realize that his antics were the result of an extremely fertile mind and a love of adventure.

Mind you, most of the time Cecil was just plain bad. He dreamed up grandiose schemes that usually involved the weakest of the lot of us who had neither the strength nor the will to disobey him. A tall, lanky classmate, Cecil could intimidate with just a simple gesture or glance.

His favourite trick was to take two or three thumbtacks and place them strategically on the seat of someone's desk while that person was at the blackboard. And he had this marvellous talent of doing his deeds unnoticed. My brother Emerson had tried the tack trick once, only to be caught by the teacher, which meant a hand spanking with the long cat-o'-nine-tails that hung on a nail beside her desk. Now, Cecil would have accomplished the deed, and not a soul would have known he had done it.

I can remember one day, however, when he paid the price.

We had just started back to the Northcote school after Christmas holidays. As usual, there were two or three beginners being instructed in the Primer book. They were tiny children, terrified for their lives, and in such awe of the school and the teacher that not one even asked to go to the bathroom.

One must understand that Miss Crosby, that stern but wonderful teacher who nurtured my entire family through the primary grades, felt duty bound to make sure that every pupil had a good grasp of the lessons. Her speech on opening day never varied: "If you don't understand the Primer book, you'll never understand grade one." This statement never failed to put the fear of the Lord into every last pupil who was in the classroom for the very first time as they envisioned spending the rest of their days in the two front desks.

On this particular day in question, one of the youngsters was not at school, which meant the long desk shared by two of them held only one Primer student. Miss Crosby asked this one pupil to come to the blackboard to trace the first three letters of the alphabet. Their backs were to the class. Cecil, as quietly as a doe picking its way through long grass, sneaked up to the empty seat and put a couple of thumbtacks where minutes before a young bottom had been. My blood was racing in my ears as I imagined what would happen when the tiny pupil and the thumbtack connected. Every eye in the school was on the two backs at the front.

Then the instruction was over, and Miss Crosby was saying, "Now let's try it in your scribbler." They both headed for the empty seat. But this time the pupil chose to enter from the other side and, to our horror, we saw Miss Crosby about to lower her frame into the seat that held the tack. We all sucked in our breaths. Cecil started to crack his toes in his gum rubbers, which he always did when he was excited.

Miss Crosby connected with the tack. She sprang from the desk like an antelope. The Primer student flew out the other side, and we could all see the bright, shiny tack still embedded in the back of Miss Crosby's silk, patterned dress. She gave her seat a couple of swipes with her hand, but the tack hung firm. Marguerite, who was in a class by herself when it came to patronizing the teacher, rushed to her rescue and gently plucked the tack from the back of the dress. She then marched right down to Cecil's desk and said in a sweet, high-pitched voice, "I think this is yours."

Miss Crosby dismissed the entire school for an early recess and then grabbed Cecil by one big, cauliflower ear, dragging him up to her desk. We all made a bee-line for the door. No sooner were we outside then we heard the whacks of the big, leather strap connecting with Cecil's giant of a hand. We doubted he would even flinch, and my brother said Miss Crosby probably had to stand on her chair to reach him.

Instead of the incident being a lesson to Cecil, he went on to place many a tack on the old, worn seats of the double desks at the Northcote school. But most of us were wise to his tricks, and we soon learned to take a good look before we slid in. You would think that a thrashing from the teacher would humble the Northcote boy but, like a cowboy adding notches to his gun, Cecil seemed to grow in stature every time he and the old cat-o'-nine-tails connected.

The spanking new coat

The big, aluminum-lined tea boxes that regularly came filled with our cousins' hand-me-downs rarely included anything that could be used by the females in our family. However, on more than one occasion I was forced into a boy's suit that hadn't a prayer of stretching to fit one of my older brothers.

My sister, Audrey, and I gradually came to accept that the box from Regina would hold treasures for the boys. As Aunt Lizzie had two sons — who we long ago had decided were probably the richest kids in their city — there wasn't much chance of us receiving anything.

One year, when the snow was piled high in the county but signs of Spring were in the air — we had seen a robin on the way to school one day and the water was starting to run in the ditches along the Northcote road — the stationmaster in Renfrew called to say, "It's here." This was all we needed to send us scurrying to the station for the big, wooden box of treasures that had been delivered from the west.

After supper the box was pushed into the centre of the kitchen floor, and Father pried off the lid with the crowbar. As was Aunt Lizzie's custom, a long letter was pinned to the top garment. It explained with minute detail the history of each piece of clothing contained in the box, and who Aunt Lizzie thought the pieces might fit. Rarely was she ever right. In our household, when it came to sorting through the hand-me-down box, one rule prevailed: "If it fits, it's yours."

Just as we were getting to the bottom of the box, Emerson pulled out what was obviously a woman's dress coat. It was grey-black, and it was the most stylish coat I had ever seen. Grey fur circled the collar, and two big patches of the same fur were sewn onto the sleeves as well. These patches were like large triangles with the points reaching almost to the elbows. The coat could have been brand new, as if it had never been on Aunt Lizzie's back. (On seeing the coat, Father started into his tirade again about how Aunt Lizzie did not know the value of the dollar and was probably spending Uncle Jack's money faster than he was making it. Our family had long ago decided that Uncle Jack made buckets of money working as a railroader with the CPR. After all, did he not have a free pass for him and his family when they wanted to travel anywhere in Canada?)

Mother pulled the coat from the box. In spite of the long trip from the west and packed in with dozens of other garments, the coat was barely wrinkled. This was a sign of a good hand of cloth, commented Mother. I could see that Audrey was eyeing the coat, but our mother said it was too old a style for a young girl. She had stood up from the kitchen chair and was examining the coat's every detail.

Now, Aunt Lizzie was a tall, thin, statuesque woman while Mother was tall and portly. I knew she was mentally measuring the girth of the fur-trimmed coat. Mother then took off her sweater and laid it over the edge of the box; we were all silent, as if we were watching a movie. She slipped her arms into the sleeves, which were full. The collar could be snugged to her neck. Mother ran her hands over the big, shiny buttons that marched down the front of the coat like soldiers.

It was soon obvious to all of us that Mother would never in a hundred years get the buttons to meet the buttonholes. But, with excitement in her voice, Mother said, "I think it could be worn either way. It doesn't have to be buttoned, you know." She struggled with the two edges of the opening, but they missed by a good six inches. Audrey had the temerity to suggest the coat would probably fit her better and that if the coat wasn't meant to close why were there big, silver buttons running up the front.

Mother told Audrey to put the kettle on to boil as she needed a cup of tea. This was her way of telling us that the subject was closed.

For the next half hour Mother wore the coat around the house — just to get the feel of it. I had to admit she looked handsome in it, but I could tell that Audrey was sadly disappointed. Eventually, Mother hung the coat on a wire hanger behind her bedroom door, not in the hall where everyone else kept their coats. Right away this meant the coat was special and there was no doubt to whom the coat belonged.

The coming Sunday we knew the coat would be making an appearance at the Lutheran church. Mother dressed with meticulous care. Audrey and I wondered what she was going to do about the six-inch-span that separated the closings. After all, it was still winter. But Mother was nothing if not inventive. She took a long, hand-knit scarf that was the colour of the fur and hung it around her neck with the ends almost touching the hemline of the coat. Next, she anchored the scarf with two, huge pins under the coat. It looked for all the world as if the scarf was always meant to be worn this way. Audrey asked her what she would do if she had to take off the coat in church, but Mother chose not to answer.

We marched into our front pew that day as if we owned the place. I could see that Mother was thrilled with Aunt Lizzie's coat and that she was aware that every eye was on her.

Mother continued to wear the coat even though the fronts never once came anywhere to meeting. As with all the other hand-me-downs that came our way during the thirties, we never admitted that the coat once graced the back of a rich aunt from Regina. To Mother, the coat was spanking new, and whenever she wore it the sting of the Depression wasn't felt.

MOTHER IN THE FUR-TRIMMED COAT, WHICH HAD COME IN A HAND-ME-DOWN BOX FROM REGINA.

Sounds on the farm

If someone asked me what I missed most about the years I was a little girl on the farm I would answer without deliberation, the sounds. At the time they meant nothing to me. It is only now, so many years later, that those special sounds will surface and I will once again relive those carefree and happy days when we were oblivious to the poverty around us.

I treasure sounds like the lament of the Whip-poor-will as it nested in the trees near our house at night. His was a lonely song, and even now I can remember burrowing deeper in the down mattress when I heard it. He frightened me, but we missed him on the occasional night when he nested in a far-off tree and were glad when he came closer to our home. Where have all the Whip-poor-wills gone, I wonder.

I can remember those early morning sounds in our house before the grey dawn broke as my father made his way down to the kitchen. Even though I was upstairs, I could picture his every move. I could hear the papers being scrunched into a ball, the lids of the Findlay Oval being scraped over, the kindling methodically placed on top of the paper. I would lay upstairs and know that the small sticks would be put together like the rail fences that circled our farm. Then I would hear Father lift a log from the wood box, and I'd listen as the fire crackled around the kindling and the flames swished as they ate into the log. I would have the coziest feeling and doze off, knowing that in minutes those sounds would mean heat in the cold, upstairs bedroom.

And nothing in these days of modern technology will ever replace the wonderful sound of the train whistle as the old steam engine pulled the freight cars through the night. The whistle would start out faintly in the distance and by the time the train reached our crossing it was distinct and clear. Just as it left our farm, we would often hear two, short blows, and our father would say, "And hello to you, Tom." We would feel very proud that we knew the engineer who drove the train.

Never again will I hear the plop-plop of the butter churn. I could always tell when the cream was about to turn because replacing the hollow sound in the churn would be the thud as the handle and disc hit the thickening butter. I can remember not understanding why the cream turned, but marvelling at the process and loving the sounds my efforts made inside the churn. There isn't much thrill today, I'm afraid, in going to the supermarket and buying a cube of butter.

Nothing has replaced those wonderful sounds of the sleigh runners cutting through the snow on a crisp winter's night, or the wagon wheels grinding out a rhythm on a gravel road — sounds that could lull a young child to sleep sitting on her mother's lap.

And what of the frogs croaking in the swamp at night? I remember summer evenings alive with the sounds of the frogs. My brothers and sister and I would try to guess which were the bullfrogs and which were the young when we listened to them. We thought each one had distinctive croaks. Today, the frogs I occasionally hear seem tired — it's as if they are trying to say to me, "It's just too much effort."

At the time, I found no romance in the sound of the old school bell, but today I see Miss Crosby come to the top step at the front of the schoolhouse with the heavy, brass bell in her hand, and the sounds ring out loud and clear in my memory. The bell at the top of the schoolhouse was also brass, and I remember its glorious, deeper tones. And I long to hear it once again.

There are many things I do not miss about the farm — the hard labour, which was the lot of my parents, for one. But when I think of the wonderful sounds of those early years, sounds that bring back memories of special happenings, a sadness comes over me, and I mourn for that which will never return.

It takes but a moment to
Pause and reflect on my
Precious blessings.
Why then, do I sometimes
Falter and neglect to say
What is in my heart?
It is not for lack of gratitude
But for weary bones, and
Heavy eyes, and days
Stretching into night.

— Mabel Ernestine Lapointe

View from the west hill

Editorial, Design & Production	Heather Lang-Runtz
Typography & Printing	Love Printing Service Ltd.
Colour Separations	Hadwen Graphics

Wallace Enterprises